SEA SICK

THE GLOBAL OCEAN IN CRISIS

ALANNA MITCHELL

McCLELLAND & STEWART

Library and Archives Canada Cataloguing in Publication

Mitchell, Alanna
Sea sick : the global ocean in crisis / Alanna Mitchell.

ISBN 978-0-7710-6116-5

1. Ocean--Environmental aspects. 2. Marine ecology. I. Title.

GC28.M58 2009   333.91'64   C2008-904239-5

We acknowledge the financial support of the Government of Canada through the
Book Publishing Industry Development Program and that of the Government
of Ontario through the Ontario Media Development Corporation's Ontario Book
Initiative. We further acknowledge the support of the Canada Council for the Arts
and the Ontario Arts Council for our publishing program.

Printed and bound in Canada

This book was produced using ancient-forest friendly papers.

This book is printed on acid-free paper that is 100% recycled, ancient-forest friendly
(100% post-consumer recycled).

McClelland & Stewart Ltd.
75 Sherbourne Street
Toronto, Ontario
M5A 2P9
www.mcclelland.com

1   2   3   4   5   13   12   11   10   09

This book is for
James Kenneth Patterson
and his remarkable uncle
Kenneth Mark Drain

CONTENTS

LAST DAYS OF AN OCEAN SYSTEM

Tim Flannery was barefoot the evening I met him, pants rolled up to below his knees. It was dusk and we had found each other in the unlikely town of Whyalla, South Australia, where, it is said, the outback meets the sea.

Our meeting was sheer serendipity. The two of us had happened to fly into this remote town of 22,000 on the same plane the night before and he had been at meetings all day with the town's steelmaker, continuing his international *tour de force* of explaining global climate change to the public, business leaders and politicians.

His book *The Weather Makers: How We Are Changing the Climate and What It Means for Life on Earth*, Al Gore's book and movie *An Inconvenient Truth: The Planetary Emergency of Global Warming and What We Can Do About It*, and the report by Sir Nicholas Stern, the former chief economist of the World Bank, on the financial consequences of ignoring climate change have been the one-two-three punch that has convinced the public that global climate change is more than, well, hot air.

Their combined effect—in concert with Hurricane Katrina's devastating tear through New Orleans in August 2005—has been remarkable. As I researched this book across five continents and over two and a half years, everyone I spoke with could pinpoint the moment that the public discourse changed from whether or not global climate change was real to what humanity needed to do about it: the third quarter of 2006, after the cumulative effect of Katrina, Flannery, Stern and Gore.

So Flannery, an Australian ecologist, is a hero to people like me who also write books about the environment. I had been hoping to meet him because he got it so right.

Plus, Flannery has done three things that other brilliant scientific minds rarely do: he has been able to put together an integrated picture of what the science is telling us, explain the implications of that big picture and then help people hear the story of those implications.

He is, in effect, a prophet who is taken seriously, who somehow happened to show up at the right time and be able to tell his story in the right way. A historically rare entity.

When we met he was longing to walk on the beach, so out we went to the sandy shore of the Spencer Gulf that runs in front of the Foreshore Motor Inn, Whyalla's finest accommodation, where the steel company had put him up.

I talked and talked, telling him about this book, the stories of my travels around the world, the scientists I had met, the questions I still had, and, above all, why it matters so much to me that all the things I have found out become part of this new, informed public discourse for which he helped lay the groundwork.

I told him of my worries.

The global ocean makes up 99 per cent of the living space on the planet, thanks to its immense depth. If you add up all the land surface and the narrow band of the atmosphere that supports creatures who breathe air, the total represents just 1 per cent of the areas where life can survive on the planet. The rest is in the ocean, covering more than seven-tenths of the earth's surface.

Even more significant than the ocean's breadth and width is its depth, or third dimension. That total volume, with its immense biological importance, is what I came to think of as the deeps, both the source of life and the future of life on the planet.

The issue is that all over the world ocean scientists, in groups of specialists who rarely put their information together, are finding that global climate change and other human actions are beginning to have a measurable effect on the ocean. The vital signs of this critical medium of life are showing clear signs of distress.

That's because roughly a third of the carbon dioxide that humans are putting into the atmosphere has entered the ocean. In addition, about 80 per cent of the extra heat being created by climate change has been absorbed by the ocean.

These two phenomena—carbon dioxide and heat—are changing the ocean's acidity, patterns of saltiness, temperature, volume, ice cover, function within the planet's carbon and oxygen cycles, and possibly the physical structure of the currents as well. And these are just the ones we happen to know a bit about.

This change is happening all over the world. And this is having a profound effect on many of the creatures that live in the ocean. At the same time, our search for food from the sea has resulted in the removal of massive quantities of creatures from the global ocean. In itself, that's a problem. And it's exacerbated by the changes we're also causing through carbon dioxide and heat, because life in the sea helps regulate the sea's physical and chemical properties. When we remove so much life, we're also removing one of the ways in which the ocean can keep its systems stable.

This is so important—and so different from the way that most of us see the issue—that some scientists I have met argue that instead of calling this the age of 'global climate change', we should call it the era of 'global ocean change' or 'marine climate change'. These terms are both much more accurate and more worrisome.

The ocean is built to withstand change. It has layers of safe-guards that the atmosphere and the land systems do not, and yet even these are being breached. It is a larger and more serious problem than atmospheric change.

However, we are not hearing much about it, or about the impli-cations for life on the planet—not just human life and civilisation, but life in general. We hear from time to time about overfishing, or about the cities that would flood if the sea level rose, or about coral bleaching, but rarely everything put together.

The first scientific attempt to map the human effect on the world's ocean came out in the journal *Science* in February 2008. It found that there was no area immune from human influence and warned of the cumulative effects on the global ocean of so many con-tiguous elements of change. The first major international scientific conference to bill itself as being about the intersection of climate and oceans was in April 2008 in Hanoi; the fourth Global Conference on Oceans, Coasts and Islands. Its recommendations about what to do will not even enter the public discourse until 2009.

The fate of the sea is not part of formal global discussions about carbon dioxide reductions. Any cohesive plan to put together these pieces of information about the ocean and protect the ocean as the main medium of life on earth is in its infancy.

One of my greatest shocks as I researched this book was that as I travelled from country to country, topic to topic, research boat to research boat, and told each new group of scientists what I had been finding, each group was surprised. In other words—and with some notable exceptions—even some of the planet's top research scientists didn't have the full picture of what's going on. Each has a specialty, isolated from the larger context for the most part, without a systemic understanding of how the pieces fit together. It reminds me of that old joke about the blind philosophers, each of whom has their hand on a piece of an elephant and is trying to describe the elephant from the piece rather than the whole. This was the state of atmospheric climate change science about twenty years ago.

Tim Flannery is a thoughtful, soft-spoken man who chooses his words carefully. Like so many biologists, he notices without effort tiny details of his environment that most of us overlook.

As I spilled my tales he became fascinated with some rare blue swimmer crabs that had washed up on the beach, and he would bend down swiftly every now and again to pick one up and examine it. In my pauses he gave elegant natural history lessons on the mangroves we could spot from the beach and how isolated they were from other patches of the world's mangroves.

He stopped to chat with some men who were fishing for sport, peering into their buckets and joking with them. His pockets bulged with pieces of giant squid cartilage half the size of boomerangs, marked by the teeth of dolphins. He handed me one or two, wondering out loud whether the dolphins ate the squid or just played with them.

Offhandedly, almost, he started to talk about the ocean, assembling disparate bits of information from his vast mental library.

About 250 million years ago, during the time known as the Great Dying at the end of the Permian period—the biggest mass extinction the world has yet known—the ocean's oxygen ran out. There are a couple of theories about why this happened, but a leading candidate is that the surface layer warmed up enough and became salty enough to disturb the currents. Currents feed oxygen from the atmosphere into the ocean and move nutrients around. When the oxygen vanished, most life on land and in the sea—more than 90 per cent of the species then alive—died.

The point of the story, he said, is that it is clear that the ocean contains the switch of life. Not land, nor the atmosphere. The ocean. And that switch can be flipped off.

We know it's happened in the past, he told me. We just don't know the trigger.

Flannery pointed out that oxygen levels in the deep waters of the Southern Ocean around Antarctica have dropped about 3 per cent in the past decade. He continued, building his case methodically. The atmosphere is 500 times smaller than the ocean, by mass, and during his lifetime of just a few decades, the atmosphere had sustained three separate and severe man-made assaults: acid rain, the ozone hole and increased carbon dioxide levels.

Those assaults had taken place when the polluting substances could be measured in the atmosphere in parts per million. Today, changes to the composition of the atmosphere can be measured at levels of parts per 10,000—two orders of magnitude larger than those earlier catastrophes.

Flannery stopped, breathing in the salty sea air, marvelling at the sun as it set over the very ocean we were discussing. 'Look at the sky,' he said, pointing to the glorious oranges, pinks, purples, blues, a huge smile on his face. 'Look at the colours.'

I still wasn't getting it. I understood the separate ideas, but not the larger message. The point, Flannery said as we started walking back to the motor inn, is that changes to the atmosphere are serious, as his own book had shown, but that changes to the ocean are far more so. The ocean is a bigger system. It's more critical to the life support of the planet. And the changes that once affected only the atmosphere are now big enough to impact on the ocean.

He told me that I was documenting the last days of a system. Humans are now interfering with the most basic elements of that system.

Keep going, he adjured me as we reached the inn's lounge, where he bought me a fortifying glass of Australian white wine.

'Just keep going,' he said, still barefoot, 'if for no other reason than that I need to read this book.'

I think often of Flannery and our walk on the beach at Whyalla, now that I am back in Canada trying to make sense of what I have learned and put it into this book.

This book did not start out to be the chronicle of a dying system or, to put a different face on it, one that is switching. It started because I became fascinated with the ocean as a global system while I was working on my last book, which was about environmental problems on land.

I was on the final journey of that book—on a research boat in the Galapagos—when I ran into Sylvia Earle. She is one of the world's most famous scientists, a marine biologist and deep-sea diver who revolutionised the way we understand ocean life by watching it where it lives rather than hoisting it up out of the water and examining it in a lab.

I was bunking with her on the ship, thinking about the black islands of the Galapagos and their amazing plants and animals. I still considered the ocean to be more or less a two-dimensional transport route with an amusing roster of animals near the surface. But since I am a journalist I started asking her questions about why she became a biologist. She answered me patiently. Finally, I asked: *But why a marine biologist? Why not look at creatures on land?* Because, she answered neatly, stopping me in my tracks, the ocean is where most of the life is.

I had never looked at it this way. Being a creature of land and a student of the land's life forms, I had never thought a lot about the ocean or the fact that life on land is utterly dependent on the life and chemistry in the ocean.

As I've discovered since, plankton produce half the oxygen we breathe or, put another way, every second breath we take. These microscopic creatures are the real lungs of our planet. The ocean controls climate and temperature and the carbon and oxygen cycles of the planet, as well as other chemical systems that give all living creatures life—including us.

Earle's concern then was the human tendency to use the ocean as an endless sewer and grocery store, dumping our waste in it and catching food recklessly. Even those few years ago, it was not clear that the ocean system was switching.

So I finished writing my last book and started reading up on the ocean. This was an act of courage. I have been afraid of water since I was a toddler and nearly drowned in an undertow on summer vacation. My parents, sitting on the beach a couple of metres from me, watched me go down and then bob up a couple of times before they realised that I was in trouble. My father dashed in and pulled me out, saving my life. I don't remember the incident, but sometimes I wonder if terror that strong and that primal is stored in the depths of the brain. Certainly it pounced on me at the most surprising moments while I pondered the fate of the sea for this book, and only while I was immersed in water.

Like so many through the ages, though, just as I feared the ocean, I was beguiled by it. Not just by its mystery or its back-drop for the collective human imagination, but by the fact that we barely even understand that it is a single, interconnected system, much less one so critical to our own survival.

At first I felt like an explorer, immersed in a growing under-standing of the sheer physicality of the ocean: how the currents move and shunt heat and cold around; how the thin layer of mol-ecules at the surface of the water breathes into a similarly slender layer at the bottom of the atmosphere, creating the chemical soup that allows life.

I read in awe of the complicated architecture of the deep ocean floor, where the earth's surface plates are dying and being born, and where the planet's largest mountain range—unseen by all but a handful of humans, and unimagined by most of us—runs like a backbone up and down the centre of the open ocean between the Americas on one side and Europe and Africa on the other.

It was a new, secret planet hidden in the world I thought I knew well, that I had spent the better part of a decade exploring and writing about. It was intoxicating.

At the same time, the Census of Marine Life began a billion-dollar worldwide exercise to figure out what lives in the global ocean—it was a pioneering human undertaking, aided by new techniques used to read each creature's DNA and trace its path backwards to the origins of life. Month after month new ocean creatures have been discovered, new clues mined about how life as it is now came to be and therefore, possibly, where it might go next.

Finally, though, it was the chemistry and physics of the ocean that captured me and held on. I am no chemist and certainly no physicist. My first degree is in English and Latin literature, and my second in journalism. But one book—which I found in Bocas del Toro, Panama, at the Smithsonian Tropical Research Institute's station there—seemed to reach out and grab me by the throat. It was *Air and Water: The Biology and Physics of Life's Media*, by Mark W. Denny.

Denny writes, crisply, that all living things on this planet live in one of two fluid media—either water or air. Of these, as I mentioned above, water is by far the larger, making up 99 per cent of the living space on the planet and home of at least half of the mass of life. This means that life is thicker on land and more spread out in the water.

Denny's book is about how the differences between air and water affect and constrain what types of life can exist in the two media. You couldn't expect a hummingbird to live in water, he points out, or a fish to live on land.

'After all, many of the basic attributes of life—the size and shape of an organism, how it moves and reproduces, how it captures food, the nature of its sensory capabilities—differ in familiar patterns depending on whether the plant or animal lives in air or water,' he writes in the introduction, adding, in a line that has become my mantra: 'In part, [this book] is an exercise in examining how a terrestrial existence has biased our perception of biology.'

For example, he points out that sea water is twenty billion times more conductive of electricity than air. It's difficult from our terrestrial perspective, as he mentions, to understand what it would feel like to be able to communicate so easily through electrical impulse. The very movement of a muscle sends out electricity that can be discerned in the ocean. What hit me like a lightning bolt in all of this was the simple concept that chemistry and physics determine biology. Therefore as chemistry and physics change, so will biology. And what I've been finding through my research for this book is that the chemistry and physics of the global ocean *are* changing.

What are the implications? What will happen to the oxygen in the ocean, the plankton that power both the biogeochemical cycle and the ocean food web? Will the ocean still support fish? Will the splendid creatures that live there now still be able to mate and produce viable young? Can humanity survive the chaos to come? And, finally, can we rein in ocean change before it's too late?

It depends on how much the chemistry and physics change. The evidence right now is that they have not changed this dramatically in about fifty-five million years, since the Palaeocene epoch lurched into the Eocene, a time of great biological upheaval. We are not talking about atmosphere or air—that secondary and important medium of life on earth—but of ocean, the primary medium. We are at a rare and frightening point in the history of life on the planet.

I came to think of this phenomenon in medical terms, because those are easier for me to understand. Like many parents I have sat through the night with a feverish, delirious baby, trying to keep the body temperature down with drugs, cool cloths, calm hands to the forehead. It's a scary place to be, especially if the child's temperature keeps rising. The danger is that if the temperature rises too high, the baby's system can't handle it and brain damage—or even death—follows. That catastrophe is relatively rare in the modern Western world, where medicine is at hand. Like many parents, I have rushed a feverish child to the emergency room for lung X-rays, the anxious needle tap of the spinal column, bags of intravenous fluid, intravenous antibiotics. And averted disaster.

What makes fever so dangerous is that the body as a whole thrives only within certain chemical and physical boundaries: its systems are set up to keep the body within those boundaries. A temperature of 40 degrees Celsius is a hand-wringer. At 41 degrees, you're at the hospital. The human body can't work very far beyond that number. Instead it hits its limit and then switches to a system that is geared toward death instead of life. The human system has chemical and physical ranges that run the gamut from optimum to impossible.

I remember a searing chemistry lesson from the day my first child was born. Throughout her gestation she had bled copiously, silently, into me through our placenta. By the time she was supposed to be born, she had little blood left in her own system, and had filled her veins and arteries with fluid to survive. Finally, still in the womb, she just stopped moving—except for her swollen heart, which kept a perilously even rhythm.

When she was born by emergency Caesarean section, her haemoglobin count was 26. It should have been 155. She was in cardiac failure, limp, chalk white, soundless. The chemistry was wrong. Through the long afternoon and evening while doctors worked to save her life, one equation kept running through my brain: *Haemoglobin, red blood cells, oxygen. Haemoglobin, red blood cells, oxygen.* How could this child survive if she had had so little oxygen?

They transfused her. She was a hell of a fighter. She survived to become a remarkable young woman. The doctors could never explain to me how her infant body had leapt over the chemical assault, only that, somehow, grace had struck.

So when I think of the planet, I think of it as a body with some serious health problems. The evidence is that the chemical levels of its ocean-blood are changing and that is affecting such things as pH, metabolism, fecundity and ability to thrive. In a growing number of places, the very oxygen content of the ocean is trailing off. These are its vital signs, and they are telling us that the planet is in distress. The planet is slipping into biological and evolutionary unconsciousness. A point of no return. A switch.

As the eminent marine biologist Jeremy Jackson of Scripps Institution of Oceanography, University of California at San Diego, wrote recently, we are creating a "brave new ocean" that, without profound and multi-faceted changes in human behaviour, will lay the groundwork for a "mass extinction in the oceans with unknown ecological and evolutionary consequences."

This doesn't mean that life will stop. It means that *life as we know it* will stop unless we can return the planet to health. But if we cannot, the components that provide the possibility for life in the future will still be here, sleeping and poised to spring back once a new system conducive to life emerges.

The medical imagery helps me understand in other ways, too. Our modern society spends billions upon billions of dollars to diagnose illness early in humans, and to treat it before it becomes acute. Think of the money for routine diagnostic breast X-rays of middle-aged women to catch breast cancer before it progresses too far—staff, hospitals, doctors to read the scans and interpret them, the machines.

Or the millions of humans on cholesterol-lowering drugs and medicine to lower blood pressure, a bid to keep their hearts from failing. Think of the industries, the science and research, the development, manufacturing and distribution know-how, the training of doctors and pharmacists that has gone into making sure that those drugs get to the humans who are supposed to benefit from them.

So I'm left with questions. If we have created modern medical systems capable of trying to prevent human illness, at the cost of many billions of dollars a year, why are we not looking at preventing—much less diagnosing and treating—the illness of the planet-body that gives us life?

The medical metaphor became particularly poignant for me as I watched scientists even in the richest countries struggle to cobble together money to conduct the research necessary to understand the planet's basic functions. The sum of a few hundred thousand dollars here or there makes a huge difference to most of these scientists and they must forsake research that funding agencies don't think is important enough. Yet these scientists are our planet's doctors and diagnosticians, the few able to read the vital signs of our life-support system and maybe, just maybe, figure out how to fix it.

Sitting in a conference centre in the Basque stronghold of Bilbao, Spain, for the research for this book, I became convinced that never in the history of human life has the work of scientists been so important to the fate of our species.

That was my lowest moment. I felt like a doomed character on an ancient quest, destined to explore the fundamental crisis of the human condition, driven to search for redemption but fated to fail.

It was another prophet who helped me climb out of that. Matthew Fox, the excommunicated Catholic priest and seer from California, showed up in my living room in frozen Toronto one Sunday morning, explaining that humans need to feel despair before they can find hope.

In Christian language, one needs the pain of loss to understand the surprising gift of resurrection. In the language of classical literature, one must lose Troy before it is possible to build Rome, or grieve over the deaths of Romeo and Juliet before reconciliation can be born. In biological terms, winter's death must come before spring's birth.

So is there hope?

You could focus on the fact that the number of scientists now involved in examining the health of the planet is growing dramatically. New findings are being announced every day. The picture is becoming clearer. The science is gelling.

You could look at the fact that, since Flannery and Gore and Stern and Katrina, it's plain that most of humanity in developed countries gets at least part of the big picture of carbon and that's different from even a couple of years ago. The dialectic has shifted, at last.

For me, it took a journey to the deeps—almost a kilometre to the bottom of the ocean—to see whether or not I could find hope. It was a scientific expedition with Harbor Branch Oceanographic Institution, a private group based in Florida, set up decades ago with a whack of money from one of the founders of Johnson & Johnson, the baby powder and pharmaceuticals company.

Just to put it in perspective, a kilometre is incredibly deep. There are parts of the ocean floor that go much deeper—to about 11 kilometres—but hardly any humans have ever voyaged to a kilometre and, as far as the Harbor Branch group knew, not a single journalist before me. The pressure at that depth is intense and would be instantly fatal if the craft sprang the smallest leak.

I was terrified. But I had spent two years obsessed with the ocean, this grand mother of life, and I simply had to be inside her, to see her for myself. I needed to bear witness to as much as I could see of this vast third dimension of the ocean that has such biological power over our planet. So I hoisted myself into the tiny aluminum chamber that was to carry me and the ship's electronics engineer down to the ocean floor. The hatch clanged shut and we lay side by side to fit.

It is pitch black at the depth of a kilometre, and it is bitterly cold. I was intently focused on the composition of the air in my aluminum womb. It became a microcosm for the chemical changes to the atmosphere and ocean that this whole book is about, to the idea that a system has limits.

I had an epiphany there. It had to do with the nature of hope. And I rolled out of my watery cradle three hours later tremulous, moved, triumphant, convinced that our species, with all its failings and trudgings, is ready for its toughest journey yet.

CHAPTER 1

THE LAST BEST PLACE ON EARTH

Great Barrier Reef

If all life on land were to vanish tomorrow, creatures in the ocean would flourish. But if the opposite happened and the ocean's life perished, then the creatures on land would die too. Life, if it went on, would have to start over.

For the vast majority of the earth's 4.5-billion-year history, the ocean was the only place in which there was life. The planet's first creatures—bacteria-like organisms stewing in a primordial soup—appeared in the ocean about 3.3 billion years ago. The first life forms on land—plants such as ferns and mosses—weren't able to exist until about 400 million years ago. Animals capable of living on land came even later.

It's hard for humans to grasp. Throughout much of our short time on the planet—perhaps 200,000 years in all—we have spun stories that tell us that the world is ours to use as we see fit.

Biologically, though, humans are here on sufferance, at the grace of the ocean. It both gives us life and keeps us alive. Two medical facts describe its metaphoric importance to humans: early-stage foetuses depend on amniotic fluid that is a chemical replica of the marine world, and the composition of our blood plasma is astonishingly similar to the composition of sea water.

However, that is not how we've viewed the sea. Since we had our first glimpse of the ocean, we've tended to see it for the other things it can give us: an endless supply of food and, later, a route to other places. We learned that the sea is useful, but we have not known until the last few generations that it is also our main life-support system, controlling the planet's temperature, climate and key chemical cycles.

Until very recently it hasn't mattered what humans think or don't think or what stories we tell. We have been inconsequential in the grand scheme of things. And what we do, or don't do, has also been insignificant, perhaps not for individual humans but for the planet as a whole and, certainly, for the global ocean. The planet's resilience, its vastness, has compensated for whatever we were doing.

What we do and how we think does matter now, though, because finally the actions and belief systems of humans are damaging the ocean. Our actions are dangerous to us and to millions of other living things. We are altering not just bits of the sea with dreadful oil spills or eroding shores or vast extinctions of fish, but the whole, interconnected global system that is the ocean, the main medium of life on earth.

As goes the ocean, so goes life. This is the axiom that, in our hubris, we have so far refused to see. We have been content to treat the ocean's mysteries as though they were immutable certainties.

Now humans must understand how the ocean is supposed to work so we can understand how our actions are damaging it. Then we'll be better equipped to stop the damage, to stand back and let the sea heal if it can. It is, as far as many scientists see, our only hope for survival.

———

One of the best places on earth to see how the ocean should work is the Great Barrier Reef, which runs down the east coast of Australia, and that's why I'm on a lurching catamaran with a few dozen seasick tourists braving high winds and roiling waves to see it.

To me this is the mother ecosystem, a modern proxy for where life must have begun, a piece of the ocean that is still gloriously intact. I have travelled around the world to savour it, as if it were a watery Paradise before the Fall, the last best place on earth.

Considered to be one of the seven natural wonders of the world, the Great Barrier Reef is by far the largest coral reef in the world, an intertwined collection of more than 2900 smaller reefs, including some of the oldest coral colonies on the face of the planet. They make a long, bony structure so substantial it can be seen from space.

It is a biological gold mine that is even more productive than tropical rainforests, arguably the most important part of the most important medium of life on the planet. This massive reef is the marine equivalent of the biggest city in the world, a vast maternity ward, the lushest, most productive and probably most complex part of the planet when you count the different types of plants and animals that live here. It is an engine of evolution.

How does it work?

The ocean is impossibly complicated, interconnected, turbulent and nonlinear, and it touches every part of life. Humans can only understand it by trying to grasp far simpler proxies. Such as: every tear you cry ends up back in the ocean system. Every third molecule of carbon dioxide you exhale is absorbed into the ocean. Every second breath you take comes from the oxygen produced by plankton.

Think of a jigsaw puzzle that works on five or six dimensions instead of just two. The pieces interconnect not in a single way, but in many.

Take the fierce winds today off the coast of Australia as a window into the complexity of this system. They are so strong that they have kept every single tourist boat along the reef at dock today—except this one, because it is a massive and fast catamaran, more powerful than other tourist craft.

To humans these high winds are an annoyance or a danger. As we boarded this morning, for example, the crew issued stern warnings about how rough the seas were and insisted that everyone take seasickness pills—either Dramamine or ginger tablets—for the hour-long journey.

One woman is crying as the catamaran heaves; she is clutching a white paper bag in case she throws up. Now a young man vanishes to the rear of the ship to peer at the horizon, a slight sweat on his upper lip. Looking at the horizon is supposed to calm a seasick stomach, but for many passengers on this boat, that trick is decidedly not working. The crew members are sighing deeply and trying to remain cheerful.

Throughout the ocean, the winds drive currents on the surface. In turn, the air and water currents move the sun's energy—or heat—from the waters of the equator to land and water further toward the poles, making the planet habitable. Some of that heat moves in great, snaking submarine rivers through the ocean basins. When the warm water, heavy with its salt, loses enough of its heat close to the poles, it descends to the abyss, depositing its heat, and then meanders back toward the Antarctic along the sea floor in a massive hemispheric conveyor belt. This is a main way that the sun's energy—the source of all life—is distributed throughout the planet.

So for every bucket of water you might collect at the seashore, individual molecules that make it up could have originated near the South Pole—where the planet's deep, cold waters are mixed as if in a huge bowl—at the equator, or in any other part of the ocean system.

Like the blood in your body, the ocean waters are constantly on the move. You have no blood that is only of the brain or only of the thumb. There is no sea water that is only of the Pacific or the Indian Ocean. There is only one ocean and it is a single system, chemically, physically and biologically.

While different latitudes of the ocean have different temperatures at the surface, and therefore support different types of life, each collection of life still supports all the others. For example, and in simplified terms, plant plankton like the cold waters of the high latitudes. They reproduce more abundantly there. But the creatures they feed, such as larger zooplankton or animal plankton, are food for krill and other little crustaceans, and they are food for little fish which, in turn, nourish the long-distance swimmers of the ocean such as tuna and marlin and sharks.

Moreover, while the surface of the ocean and the floor are different temperatures and support different creatures, again, they are joined by the winds. The very fierce winds—including hurricanes—help mix water in the surface layer with water further down. Deep water contains nutrients and chemicals that creatures at the surface, particularly plankton, need. Without wind those nutrients would stay in the deep and the plankton wouldn't be able to grow. That inability of the layers of water to mix unaided is known as stratification.

Without plankton, the food web of the ocean would collapse. All the larger creatures in the sea depend on plankton, either as their own food or as food for the creatures they like to eat.

Plankton may be at the bottom of the food chain in the ocean, but they are at the top of the biogeochemical system of the planet, meaning that they help control its carbon and oxygen cycles. They are the key to how these elements move through living creatures and through their non-living surroundings so that they can be used again by the living.

The winds also help foster the exchange that occurs when the top layer of the ocean's surface meets with the bottom layer of the atmosphere. That's where the main chemical transfer between air and water takes place. This molecules-thin layer is a vast entry point where carbon and oxygen, heat and cold, and gassy water move between sea and air.

This whole system works within an astonishingly narrow set of limits and norms that have been unchanged, in some cases, for millions of years.

For example, the ocean acid-base balance (the pH), which is intimately connected with the concentration of carbon dioxide in the atmosphere, has been about the same for more than twenty million years. In the open ocean it has historically registered 8.2 on the pH scale, meaning that the ocean is slightly basic (neutral is 7, below 7 is acidic).

At the coasts, where freshwater runs into the ocean and the assemblage of living creatures is attuned to a different pH, the water is more acidic, sometimes hovering in the range of 7.5 until it mixes with the rest of the ocean.

Outside of that range of acidity, the biological and chemical functions of the ocean don't work as well, at least not for all of the different types of creatures that are needed for the ocean system to do what it has done over time.

We arrive at the outer fringe of the northern Great Barrier Reef; just beyond us, toward the open ocean, the continental shelf plunges straight down for more than 1000 metres. In parts of the frigid waters of the abyss much further away, a new ocean floor is constantly being made by the molten mantle that seeps through the rifts.

This particular part of the northern Great Barrier is also just about as pristine as it could be, which is a rare quality in the modern world's ecosystems and especially uncommon for coral reefs, which once thrived in the warm, shallow waters that circle the earth to the north and south of the equator. Now coral reefs as a whole are considered critically endangered across the globe.

Over the past twenty years, living coral around the world has been destroyed five times more quickly than tropical rainforests. The pace of destruction has doubled in the past decade and some corals in the waters of Galapagos are near extinction. More than a quarter of the world's reefs have already been killed off and another 50 per cent are in severe trouble. In the Caribbean, which was a coral wonderland just three decades ago, 80 per cent of the reefs have died, reduced to limestone rubble and algal slime.

This level of destruction of the reefs is unprecedented in recent times. We'd have to look far back in the fossil record to see a similar coral death rate. In some of the earlier cases of whole-sale die-off, it took millions of years for the coral to come back, seeded from handfuls of hardy remnants able to survive until conditions improved again.

Unfortunately, further south on the Great Barrier Reef things are not quite so splendid, either. The worldwide decay of coral reefs—caused by pollution from land, too much fishing, nasty practices to capture wild fish for the aquarium trade and waters that are too hot because of global climate change—has already started to take its toll.

However, Turtle Bay, part of the Agincourt Reef on the outer edge of the Great Barrier, is a world of wonder. The waters are emerald green, shot through with brilliant blue. The bottom, visible among masses of corals, is white sand and only several metres below the surface.

The boat's crew is talking up the lazy turtles we can expect to see, the Volkswagen-sized clams that take two hours to shut their mouths, the shoals of brilliantly coloured tropical fish. For me, though, it's all about the corals, those ancient, primitive animals whose ancestors have been on the planet for about 450 million years.

I zip myself into my diving skin, shove my feet into the flippers I've carried halfway around the world, spit into my mask to prevent it from fogging up and plunge under the fierce waves.

It is stunning. And sheer calm after the messy voyage to get here. Katharina Fabricius, the coral scientist from the Australian Institute of Marine Science in Townsville—and my tutor and host on this trip—has given me a primer on what to look for. A few days ago at her house on Magnetic Island, she ran me through a slew of underwater photographs she'd taken. It's what she calls her 'good reef/bad reef' presentation and she's been using it since 2001 to explain to politicians and others some of the problems with today's reefs.

A good reef has lots of structure, she says, high coral cover, lots of different types of coral, lots of baby corals and lots of other marine organisms seeking shelter. A bad reef has little structure. It's flatter and has fewer types of corals, some dead corals, empty patches, few fish and baby corals smothered in mud. Go to Agincourt Reef, she advises me. It's still in great shape.

She's right: Turtle Bay is an excellent reef. If you set down a picture frame, every square centimetre would be full of corals and there would be masses of different shapes, colours and sizes. There are no patchy, thin, crumbling spots as there are on so many other coral reefs, including those I have seen in the Caribbean and Asia. No dead corals, nor the suffocating slick of big, indigestible algae.

Here are dozens of different types of hard coral, each of which has built up a substantial bony structure by cleverly using the calcium and carbon stored in the ocean. These limestone shapes will keep growing for as long as the coral animal—a thin membrane of flesh attached to the surface of the limestone—stays alive.

Some are the faster-growing branching corals, making shapes

like the limbs of trees. I can see fields upon fields of *Acropora* species, like the antlers of elk and deer, some of which are neon blue. I've seen beds of *Acropora* in the Caribbean that were nothing but skeletons rotting in the saltwater. This richness is breathtaking by contrast.

Some of the other corals here are slow-growing massive types that build the foundation of the reef. They have nooks and slits, caves and secret crevices running along the metres-high structure, each filled with other species, a riot of colour. They are like underwater coral gardens, some so close to the surface that I have to be careful not to kick them with my flippers as I snorkel over the top.

These bony shapes are necessary in order for a reef to be a home and protector and on-demand food market to the sea's creatures. All told, about a quarter of the creatures that humans catch commercially spend some part of their life cycle on a coral reef.

Once you've got the structure, as Fabricius says, the soft corals come, and the fish and the worms, the mammals and bacteria and reptiles, the birds above and all the other creatures that lay their eggs and rear their young and use the reef to survive.

The Great Barrier Reef is home to so many plants and animals that a full count has never been made, not even of the corals themselves. Many are still unknown to science and unnamed.

While the reef is critical to the survival of so many other species, though, it is also totally dependent on plants for its own survival. The coral animals that build the reef cannot exist without the brightly coloured micro-algae, called zooxanthellae, that live within their very cells. Like other plants, the microscopic algae convert energy from the sun into food through a chain of chemical reactions. The food feeds the coral animals as well as the algae. Without them, the corals starve and lose the brilliant colour the algae give them. Without the corals for protection, the algae die. It is the canonical example of a symbiotic relationship.

How well can the planet's other creatures get along without corals? What would happen to the physical, chemical and biological structures of the ocean if the reefs die? The answers are unknown.

As I snorkel here, marvelling at the virtuoso display of biological creativity, I wonder whether humans have become symbionts who have lost the knowledge that we depend on other creatures for the basics of life support. In terms of pure self-interest, this is a problem. If we depend on corals, algae, plankton and millions of other species, and if we are killing them off, how will we survive?

The textbook definition of a parasite is this: a species that thrives while its host dies. Except the host in humans' case is not a single creature but, rather, all sorts of other species and even whole ecosystems. In biological terms killing the host, or the host systems, is a risky strategy for the parasite. That is, unless there are other systems or hosts to move on to.

I wonder whether these simple, ancient animals, which do not even have brains, can remind humans about the ground rules of symbiosis and the perils of ignoring them. What if the great lesson from the Great Barrier Reef is not just that it is a vision of the unspoiled past but that it also forecasts the parable of future destruction?

In her home on Magnetic Island, Katharina Fabricius has been explaining some of what this great reef can teach humans. The reef is, in fact, where all of the pressing threats to the ocean intersect, a microcosm of the problems and also of the hopes.

A slight, athletic woman with the fine features of a runway model, Fabricius has picked me up after a long trans-Pacific flight and offered me a bed on the floor of her spare room over an Easter weekend.

It was snowing when I left Toronto. On Magnetic Island the temperature is in the thirties and sweltering. Her house is in a small thicket on this holiday island renowned for beaches, surfing and honeymoon getaways. This is the busiest weekend of the year on the island. Every hotel room is packed and the beaches are thronged with holiday-makers.

Fabricius and her partner, Glenn De'ath—also an eminent ocean scientist—dislike doors and windows and walls. Geckos, spiders, possums and the occasional snake wander in and out at will. Breezes sweep through the house. In a high corner of the porch where they eat their meals, the couple has built a shelter for tree frogs so they won't be picked off by predators. The night I arrived, awakened by thumps on the floor, drunk with jet-lag, I bolted from my room with a wavery flashlight to see that a scatter of the fat, neon-green frogs had jumped from the ceiling onto the floor of the open kitchen.

The plain fact, as Fabricius explains, is that the Great Barrier Reef is in mortal danger.

It's not just from all the obvious, localised threats that have affected so many other reefs around the world. Australia has taken a hard line against many time-honoured coral-killing practices. These include catching too many fish, trawling, long-line fishing, and using cyanide poisoning and dynamite on the reefs to catch tropical fish for the marine aquarium trade.

In fact, the Great Barrier Reef is designated an Australian National Park, protected by heavily enforced laws against those destructive practices. Fully a third of this reef is a no-take zone, meaning that no commercial activity can take place at all and that other activities are controlled. However, the biggest threats will come from what Australian law alone cannot prevent: global climate change.

Climate change has three direct effects on corals that scientists have become aware of in recent years.

First, the high concentration of carbon dioxide in the atmosphere warms the ocean to the point that the corals' symbiotic algae die. That's known as coral bleaching, because when the algae die, their colour disappears and leaves the corals' flesh ghostly white. Unless the corals can attract new algae, they starve and the flesh covering the bony skeleton rips off in shreds. In turn the skeleton, devoid of animal cover, begins to decay. Even if they can attract new microalgae, the bleached corals' ability to grow and reproduce is impaired while they heal.

Coral bleaching—which only became known as a scientific phenomenon a couple of decades ago—has been increasing all over the world as climate change takes greater hold.

On the Great Barrier Reef, waters have warmed on average less than half a degree Celsius since the end of the nineteenth century, yet bleaching has run far ahead of expectations. By the end of this century, ocean temperatures at the Reef are forecast to be between one and three degrees Celsius higher than they are now, leading to a dramatic increase in bleaching. In fact the best predictions are that by 2050, severe bleaching will be a yearly event on the Reef. With no cooler intermediate years, the corals will not be able to heal or grow back, or restore their ability to reproduce.

Second, climate change holds out the potential of increasing the volume of the sea. As land-based ice sheets in Antarctica and Greenland melt in the warmer climate, extra water will pour into the global ocean basin. It's not clear how much higher sea levels will rise or how quickly—estimates vary from less than a metre to as much as 9 metres in the coming century—but odds are that they will put many of the world's remaining healthy reefs so far underwater that the algae won't be able to catch enough of the sun's rays to photosynthesise. In effect, the corals will drown.

Third, and even more serious, are the chemical changes occurring in the ocean water itself. Scientists are calling this the big gorilla in the corner.

Atmosphere and ocean are ineluctably joined. In fact, some scientists consider them parts of the same system. They interact with each other, similar to the way the lungs exchange chemical compounds such as oxygen and carbon dioxide with blood within the body. As carbon dioxide gets stored in the atmosphere while we burn fossilised carbon in the form of coal, oil and gas, it also gets stored in the ocean. The ocean has absorbed about a third of the extra carbon that we have pumped into the atmosphere since we started using fossil fuels, digging up grasslands and cutting down forests.

Today, the proportion of carbon dioxide in the atmosphere is about 387 parts per million by volume. Before the industrial era, it was 280. The latest intergovernmental panel report on climate change has predicted that once the level reaches 450—possibly by mid-century—humans will have pushed roughly a quarter of the planet's creatures into extinction. If it reaches 550—or about double pre-industrial levels—we will have caused the genetic extermination of up to 70 per cent of living things, a massive extinction spasm and one of just five others in the planet's history.

In the atmosphere carbon dioxide is chemically inert, but it has a huge effect on climate. In the ocean carbon dioxide is chemically active. It reacts with other compounds in the saltwater to make the ocean more acidic.

The changes so far are relatively small—about a tenth of a unit of pH on average across the global ocean. That sounds tiny, but the pH scale is not straightforward. In mathematical terms it is logarithmic rather than linear, meaning that, going up the scale, each unit is 10 times as much as the unit that came before it. This means that small changes in the measurement mean enormous changes in the actual chemistry. Thus a change of a tenth of a unit represents a 30 per cent increase in acidity.

As more carbon dioxide enters the ocean, the water's acidity increases. At that stage it can absorb no more carbon. Depending on how we continue in our use of fossil fuels, the pH will have dropped by four- or five-tenths of a unit by the end of this century—a historically massive amount.

Because of the way carbon and calcium interact in the ocean waters to form new compounds, calcium will be less available to creatures that need it to make bones and skeletal structures—like corals. That means corals are not able to make reefs as quickly and that over time, as the acidity increases, they will not be able to build their structures at all.

The changing chemistry of the ocean also means that once its pH reaches a certain point, the water will become acidic enough to corrode the healthy reefs that remain. Like the ancient pearl Cleopatra famously dropped in a goblet of vinegar so she could dazzle Antony with her decadent excess, the corals dissolve.

Of course, once the corals are gone, the creatures that depend on them are gone too.

These threats are years or even decades in the future. But they *are* real, and they will compound the problems that have already caused so much death on the world's reefs. It will be a spiral that feeds on itself, magnifying the negative effects, becoming greater than the sum of its parts. So corals face not just one imminent threat but several that combine, magnifying each other to join with the severe conditions that already exist.

Unless humans find a way to halt this scenario, it will become what's known as a positive feedback system, set in motion in order to create a new system rather than preserve the old. It's a switch.

Here again, a medical metaphor: when the human body has a bacterial infection, it develops a fever to protect itself. The high temperature makes it hard for the bacteria or viruses to survive. The goal of the fever is to kill the infectious agents and restore the body to health. But if the infection rages too far and the fever goes too high, then the body switches from fostering health to courting death. Fever takes over and the body dies. A new and different system is born—decay—which is designed to break the body up into its component chemicals and offer them up for new forms of life. The old system—or body—is gone forever and cannot be recovered.

In the case of the Great Barrier Reef, the system is striving to maintain its current health. When its corals bleach horribly, as they did in 1998 and in 2002, the reef sets about healing itself, preparing to grow again. But if the predicted miseries occur—acidity, death by bleaching, drowning, more intense cyclones and the systemic disturbances that will accompany them—then the reef will move into a new mode. It will abandon the old balance. Instead of trying to preserve the regime that exists now, it will begin to help a different one come into being.

In the Caribbean, where 80 per cent of corals are dead, this is already happening. A new system has already taken over in which slimy algae are the main form of life and corals, fish and mammals are relatively rare.

Scientists believe that the corals won't be able to adapt to the onslaught of carbon dioxide if humans fail to curb emissions. The changes are happening far too quickly. Ocean chemistry, for example, is shifting more quickly than it has for millions of years. It has begun to change dramatically from decade to decade, just the blink of an eye in evolutionary terms. Most corals grow slowly, reproduce with difficulty, evolve in minuscule increments.

Corals appear to have been unable to adapt quickly to changes in ocean chemistry in earlier times of great disruption. The fossil record shows that when corals vanished they did so for millions of years at a time, coming back only because a few species held on somewhere and eventually formed new populations after painstaking adaptation.

Even if corals could evolve quickly enough to adapt to the new environment, how would they know which new system to adapt to? It's a moving target. To halt the coming damage to the reef and the multitude of creatures that depend on it, humans would have to ensure that the concentration of carbon dioxide in the atmosphere rises little higher than it is now. That means changing our sources of energy to those not based on carbon, or using them in ways that do not emit carbon into the atmosphere.

All of this is possible, Fabricius says. In fact, she argues that we have an ethical and moral responsibility to do what we can to prevent the death of the reef, with all its accompanying consequences. But to do it would take rapid changes in our belief systems. We have to understand that our population and our use of fossil energy cannot keep growing. She points across the water to the mainland. Further inland are coal mines which send boatloads of the carbon dioxide-spewing fuel to China.

She shakes her head. Australians glory in their powerful economy, which is strong partly because it provides a climate- and ocean-altering fossil fuel to another country. We are holding onto a belief in growth that was born hundreds of years ago, she says. But the climate and ocean system are changing in ways they have not for millions of years.

Tradition, she believes, will trump reason on this issue, with catastrophic results. We haven't learned how to take the long view.

Back at Turtle Bay we're having a rough time snorkelling. The winds have whipped the heavy waves into a frenzy. Saltwater splashes through the breathing tube into the mouthpiece, forcing us to surface quickly and frequently, and gulp desperately for air. Our umbilical cords to the surface are treacherous.

I know that our own blood plasma is chemically a dead ringer for sea water—a legacy of the fact that all creatures, including our ancestors, evolved in the ocean—but as I spit out another mouthful of salty water I am forcibly reminded that this is no longer our medium of life. It is a foreign and a frightening place where humans have few defences.

We're being bounced along by the energy of the waves, too. I have to learn to let myself go, to try not to fight against the water or control it. I cannot bend it to my will.

Being here requires humility.

I've just spotted a green turtle swimming smoothly among the gorgeous swathes of coral. It's fully a metre across, as big as a dining room table. I swim beside it for a while, envious of its easy movement, the graceful paddle of its feet, the ballet it can dance underwater.

I'm careful not to swim above it. That can spook them and sometimes they panic, dive deep and suffocate before they can get back to the surface.

Like so many types of sea turtles, the greens are globally endangered, often killed by long-line fishing techniques and by people who crave their meat and eggs. One of its common names in French is *tortue comestible*, or the turtle that's good to eat. Only about 200,000 nesting females are still alive anywhere in the world.

Over here is a long, ribbon-thin neon yellow fish with a black eye and a mouth like a flute. Here, a clutch of giant clams, some with intensely blue lips. And everywhere, schools of fish in colours that bring to mind candy shops and party frocks.

We're out of the water now. We've had to abort a snorkel further down Agincourt Reef at a fish hot spot known as Castle Rock. By now, at the end of the day, the waves are just too heavy, the wind too strong.

I've peeled out of my diving suit and am in dry pants and a shirt. Despite the heat of the day I am shivering in my warm jacket. Being in the ocean for hours on end gives a chill to the bone. My skin smells like salt and fish. Little abrasions I had before I went in are healed up as if they had never existed.

A photographer who has dived with us today and snapped our pictures underwater is flogging DVDs, complete with pictures from the Agincourt Reef that he and others took before this trip. I notice that they're mainly of fish. The corals could be so much wallpaper.

This tourist outfit, Quicksilver Group, is superb. It is renowned in the scientific community for its help with marine research. Its literature boasts that it has Australia's largest team of marine biologists outside of government agencies. Yet there has been not a single mention of the threats the reef faces, apart from adjurations not to touch it or cart any of it away because of the hefty fines, as if tourists were the greatest danger.

I think about the meeting I had yesterday with Paul Marshall and Johanna Johnson in Townsville. They work for the Great Barrier Reef Marine Park Authority assessing the effects of climate change on the reef, part of a larger Australian team working on the research on this topic. They have international reputations in their field. And they are frank about the fact that they are buying time for the reef. That means limiting fishing, restricting shipping and other local forms of damage to the reef.

The theory is that if the stresses that can be controlled are kept to a minimum, the reef has a better chance to survive the massive stresses still to come as the climate continues to change.

The guiding principle is that if any reef in the world has a chance to survive what's coming, it's the Great Barrier Reef, and these scientists and their park authority are going to give it every possible chance.

Marshall lists all the natural advantages of the Great Barrier Reef compared to other reefs, when it comes to outright survival.

First, its sheer size means that bits of it might remain after destruction, to start anew.

Next, water circulation—and, therefore, the free movement of creatures—around the reef is high. There's always the chance that if nothing there survives, a new reef could be seeded from something that survived somewhere else.

There's also the fact that relatively few people live close to the reef. The amount of chemical pollution and silt from industry and farming is lower than it would be if Australia were as thickly populated near its coast as, say, Indonesia or Florida.

Plus the Reef is fabulously rich in species, seeded from the reefs of Papua New Guinea further north. Some coral reefs don't start out with nearly this much. The more species there are, the greater the likelihood that some of them will survive.

One of the terms that keeps coming up in our conversation is 'refugia'. It refers to little clusters of genetic coral material that will slip through the cracks of destruction and live to build another reef. Marshall and Johnson are counting on a few little bits of reef being left somewhere.

Still, they know that the Great Barrier Reef is in for some severe changes in the coming years. It's locked in, as they put it. Already Australia's monsoon season has begun to fail. That means clouds are vanishing and the temperature of the air, the sand and the water is rising. There's also less wind to cool things down.

They can already see changes in the system reflected in what's happening with sea birds and sea turtles. In 2005, which was the hottest year on record on the Great Barrier Reef, baby birds died en masse. At first the scientists thought the chicks died of exposure in the torrid heat. But it turned out that the problem was something quite different. The waters on the reef were so hot that the plankton moved to cooler places and the fish followed. So when the mother sea birds went foraging for food to feed the chicks, the little fish weren't there. The chicks died of starvation.

For the sea turtles 2005 held a different, but equally grisly, fate. When scientists couldn't figure out where all the baby turtles were at Mon Repos beach, the largest mainland turtle rookery in Australia, they began searching the nests. They found cooked eggs. It had been so hot that the eggs had baked instead of hatching.

Marshall sees hope, though. Scientists have a huge role to play in crafting programs to remove what stresses they can and in pooling knowledge to find solutions for the problems of the Reef. He likens it to a Darwinian age, an era of scientific discovery.

'Even if we can make the difference between 5 per cent coral cover and 15 per cent, it's well worth our while,' he says.

I look around me at these reef aficionados on the catamaran, munching on their sweets and cheese. What would they do if they knew all this? Would they be shocked? Would they make a ruckus, push for solutions?

I have the absurd urge to get up and shout, 'Does anybody on this catamaran know what's going on here or why it matters?' Instead, I vow to team up with a group of scientists who will be examining parts of the Gulf of Mexico that have lost their oxygen for more clues about how this complex ecosystem works. Those parts are devoid of life. I will voyage from this Eden to a dead zone.

Afternoon tea is ending. The crew is again handing out doses of Dramamine and ginger for the rough trip back to the mainland. We will speed bravely, boldly, through the stiff waves over the corals, the turtles, fish, sharks and giant clams. It will be as though we were never here.

Already, many of the passengers are dozing.

CHAPTER 2

READING THE VITAL SIGNS: OXYGEN

Gulf of Mexico: The line between life and death in the blob

Not far from New Orleans, where the mighty length of the Mississippi River goes off like a fire hose into the Gulf of Mexico, lies the blob.

The blob is thick and dense, a shape-shifting layer of water which is short on oxygen stuck under the surface of the Gulf. Parts of it have no oxygen at all, an astounding phenomenon for such an energetic part of the global ocean.

Conceptually, the blob is like those lava lamps from the 1960s. When they were plugged in, heat from the lightbulb melted wax which then formed funky three-dimensional shapes inside a cone of coloured liquid. The blob is like the wax, forming a different size and shape each year. Right now it's massive, settled thickly on 17,000 square kilometres of the Gulf's sea floor and in places rising nearly to the surface in an unmixable mass.

I'm with a group of American scientists who have allowed me to join them on a scientific expedition to examine the blob in detail for the first time. We'll be sampling meticulously mapped sections of it, as well as water outside its edges, to measure the difference the lack of oxygen makes to what can live in the water column. It will take us eleven days of around-the-clock work at sea to gather data from a small portion of the blob.

The issue with the blob is that without oxygen there are no fish or shellfish. When fishermen trawl the bottom for fish, shrimps and crabs, they get nothing. That's why they call the blob 'the dead zone'.

However, it's not exactly clear if the area is entirely dead or whether something might live in the rest of the water column, only some of which lacks oxygen. So the questions in play here during this trip are what, exactly, can live in little or no oxygen, and how does the extent of the dead zone affect the creatures that ought to be here? Do they suffocate, or pool at the edges of the blob where the oxygen shows up again, or swim in and out through the water column that runs from the ocean floor to the surface? Does the normal collection of creatures change for good? Does it affect the overall capacity of the fabulously rich Gulf of Mexico to support life? What are the implications?

The Gulf of Mexico's dead zone is one of about 407 in the world, a figure that has doubled each decade since 1960. This one, running off the southern coasts of Louisiana and Texas, is among the most highly studied in the world. There are still many, many questions about how dead zones work, but recently it has become far more imperative to build on what is already known about this one. That's not just because these zones are spreading throughout the global ocean from chemicals we are putting in the water, but also because several extraordinary new dead zones have emerged that, to the astonishment of scientists, are directly related to global climate change.

One big surprise is the low-oxygen zone just discovered at the northern edge of the California current system off the western coast of the United States of America. This is a huge, rich part of the global ocean that has not been known to have low oxygen before, and one of just four major eastern boundary current systems in the world.

These four—including the California, the Benguela of the south Atlantic off Africa, the Humboldt of the southeast Pacific and the Canary off the northwest coast of Africa—are among the most productive parts of the global ocean and are driven by the winds. When the winds whip up the currents, the water brings key nutrients including nitrogen and phosphorus from the deep ocean to the sunny surface to feed plankton and other creatures. But when the wind patterns change, as they have begun to do, this alters circulation patterns. The level of nutrients can change too, leading to low oxygen.

That's what's happened off the northwest coast of the US in six consecutive years, starting in 2001, where a low-oxygen zone spread through the water column and stayed for months at a time, leaving the area devoid of fish and causing a mass dying-off of crustaceans.

A similar phenomenon is happening in both the Humboldt and the Benguela eastern boundary current systems. The implications are frightening, because they point to the possibility that the low-oxygen zones will spread rapidly, abruptly changing parts of the ocean critical to the marine food web.

Scientists are also finding that vast oxygen-starved zones in the deep waters of the Pacific and Atlantic Oceans are expanding. They are thickening and moving nearer to the surface, the direct result of the climate change that is warming the ocean. In turn that keeps the colder, even deeper waters—which contain all the food and nutrients necessary for plankton—segregated from the surface. It's reminiscent of the Permian extinction from 250 million years ago, when ocean life nearly died out.

These are the unpredictable systemic ocean changes that Tim Flannery warned me about in Whyalla—the potential triggers for a widescale ocean system switch.

For me, the dead zone is where all the themes of the ocean switch converge. It is the story of what happens when humans push a living system past its limits to the point that its chemistry goes wrong and a new system begins.

Dead zones are a chemistry problem. In the Gulf of Mexico, this is how it works. The iconic Mississippi River, which divides America roughly in half, has the third largest drainage basin in the world after the Amazon and Congo rivers. Each spring as American farmers sow their crops on farms that line the tributaries of the Mississippi, they top them up with synthetic nitrogen fertilisers, as well as phosphorus.

Over the past five or six decades, as the American population has grown, this load of agricultural chemicals has increased by a factor of at least three. Those chemicals, far in excess of the amount nature creates on its own, run off the land into the tributaries and collect in the Mississippi, which then sweeps them down to its mouth near New Orleans and deposits them in the Gulf of Mexico.

The plankton and bacteria take it from there. Nitrogen and phosphorus are super-food for plankton—the ocean's tiny plants— just as they are for the plants the farmers are trying to grow as crops up river. Therefore, the plankton gobble it up, reproduce like crazy, then die and fall to the bottom of the Gulf's continental shelf.

At the bottom the dead plankton become a feast for bacteria, which go on an eating and decomposition rampage. They multiply exponentially and use up all the oxygen. In this part of the ocean, the ability of the ocean to handle all that extra food has failed. It has reached its limit.

Under most circumstances this wouldn't be a problem, because a fresh supply of water and oxygen from the ever-flowing ocean would rush in and restore the balance. But here in the vast Gulf, that micro-organistic gluttony happens in layers of water that stubbornly decline to mix. In fact, it often takes a storm or hurricane to get the layers churned up again and put oxygen back into the water column. Failing that, the blob dissipates on its own over the winter once farmers stop adding nitrogen and phosphorus to their lands. It re-emerges each spring.

Some of the other 407 or so dead zones have different sources. Sometimes the nitrogen feast comes from industry, human waste or the chemicals that settle in river basins from the burning of fossil fuels, rather than from the 120 million tonnes of agricultural fertiliser used each year around the world.

Dead zones in these once-productive coastal seas were all but unknown until after World War II. The United Nations Environment Programme, which tracks the zones, has warned that their number is poised to escalate rapidly and that dead zones will greatly endanger humanity's ability to feed on fish in this century—and that's separate to the parts of the ocean where oxygen has gone missing due to climate change.

The Gulf's dead zone is the second largest in the world and one of the most highly studied. The Gulf is one of America's most productive fishing areas, with nearly $1 billion worth of fish and shellfish caught each year, or about a fifth of all the marine creatures caught in US waters. Government officials—who finance most of the research—are keen to make sure that the dead zone doesn't interfere too much with tonnage.

Stu Ludsin, a thirty-something triathlete who is a fisheries biologist at Ohio State University's Aquatic Ecology Laboratory and was earlier with the US Government at the Great Lakes Environmental Research Laboratory in Ann Arbor, Michigan, is the chief scientist for the expedition. It's his first time in the role and he will be conducting his own research as well as plotting the course for the trip, consulting with the ship's crew and mediating any disputes among the scientists' big personalities.

Tonight, here at Cocodrie, Louisiana, a stone's throw from the Texas border, we are loading the *Pelican*, the research vessel that will be our home for the next eleven days, with truckloads of underwater measuring and trawling devices, computer equipment, a chest freezer and lab paraphernalia for the three teams of scientists on this trip. This activity involves winches, hard hats, duct tape and immense amounts of sweat in this drenched bayou night.

Ludsin—who recently competed in a triathlon in New York City that included swimming in the crazily polluted Hudson River, and who is still talking about the sludge he had to extract from his ears and nose—is not keen to lose his training edge. So, from the van and trailer that he has driven from Michigan, he pulls out his bike with a stand that will turn it into a stationary rider, hoists it onto his shoulder and carries it up to the chief scientist's stateroom.

William Boicourt and Mike Roman, two senior scientists from Horn Point Laboratory at the University of Maryland Center for Environmental Science, are familiar with the exigencies of being chief scientist on such a complex expedition; they nudge each other over the optimism Ludsin's action betrays, but remain mute.

Frank Jochem from Florida International University (he's since moved to private industry to make biofuels from algae) and Peter Lavrentyev from the University of Akron in Ohio are the experts who will track the fate of microplankton in the dead zone. Tonight they are reverently unpacking a new FlowCAM for its first test run. Using a laser beam it will count, examine, photograph and sort some of the tiniest creatures in the ocean in a flow of ocean water piped in from outside the ship.

Until recently, Jochem tells me, scientists couldn't see these tiny plankton alive in the wild. They were just brownish blobs, dead on a slide under a microscope. Now, with this beauty he's unwrapping from its factory packaging, he'll be able to see not only what's there, but also its colour and shape, and a raft of other characteristics.

This will allow him to link what's happening on a microbial level in the dead zone with what's happening with all the larger creatures. It's like finding a critical piece of a puzzle that hadn't been available before and being able to put it with all the other pieces.

In another air-conditioned lab a couple of metres away on the other side of the *Pelican*, Roman and Boicourt are duct taping laptops onto the counters. I count eight. These will read the information on the larger algae and zooplankton that the pair and their team will collect with an instrument that flies through the water column in smooth waves from near the bottom to near the top. It's called ScanFish and Boicourt, who has babied it through fieldwork, breakdown and crisis for fifteen years, is anxious to make sure it's in top shape.

Ludsin and his team of grad students are going to be trawling for fish both in the middle of the water column and at the bottom. They're in for the heavy lifting and the fish guts rather than the more high-tech enterprises of the other teams.

It's late. Everyone is exhausted. We pile into our bunks and sleep if we can as the *Pelican*, clanging with unfamiliar noises, makes its way to the dead zone.

On the first full day on board the focus is on the figure of 2 milligrams of oxygen per litre. That figure is the dividing line between life and death in the ocean. Below 2 mg animals—including fish—can't live. Above 2, they can. We are right in the centre of the dead zone, so the oxygen is uniformly below 2 throughout the irregular mass of the blob.

Roman and I will be a team for the rest of trip, logging two shifts a day of four hours each, mainly monitoring ScanFish. He's teaching me the ropes.

ScanFish measures depth, salinity, temperature, oxygen, conductivity, time and fluorescence. The latter is a proxy for the amount of plankton in the water column. Later Roman, Boicourt and their team will analyse their findings to figure out what's in the water and how it relates to the oxygen levels.

Part of the scientific method is to find out something and then see if you can confirm the findings another way. For that reason, this floating laboratory is set up so that different instruments can examine the dead zone at the same time but from different perspectives. So in addition to using several instruments to check the water for its chemical properties, physically taking water samples, looking at the plankton through the FlowCAM, trawling for fish, and using ScanFish to examine algae and zooplankton, we are also measuring the amount of fish in the water column using acoustics.

This instrument stays in the water almost all the time, scattering sound waves that bounce down and come back up. The waves are then translated into colours on a screen that give a picture of the life in this part of the ocean. If the screen is red, that means there's lots of life. Bits of green mean that there's something in the water column. If it's blue, there's nothing.

Right now there's a lot of blue in a thick layer on the bottom. It's spooky: this part of the ocean ought to be teeming with life.

Ludsin is out on deck in the torrid heat getting ready for his inaugural trawl. He has a vast net attached to a set of heavy doors, which keep the net's mouth wide open, and chains to take it to the bottom. It's a cumbersome and dangerous rig that could easily crush a foot. Clad in hard hats and neon orange life jackets, he and several men winch up the net and manoeuvre it into the water behind the *Pelican*, tail first.

Ludsin is standing there in his Wellington boots and his garden gloves to protect himself from jellyfish stings when the net comes back up fifteen minutes later. He has a red and white cooler at the ready for any fish he wants to preserve for further study. He hoists the trawl onto the deck and sorts through the catch.

In a healthy part of the Gulf there would be hundreds of kilograms of assorted fish, likely small ones that school in tight clusters near the bottom. He has several jellyfish, which do well in low oxygen, and an Atlantic bumper fish maybe 2 centimetres across that got caught in the mesh.

Roman peers at it. 'Put 'im on a cracker and I'll eat 'im,' he says.

Ludsin, who hasn't slept in thirty hours, is discouraged. Why aren't there any fish at all—not even those that could live *above* the dead zone? It's clear that the lack of oxygen has made the fish change their behaviour, but it's not at all clear what that will mean to the fish over time. How much of their life's energy are they investing in leaving this part of the sea and finding somewhere more hospitable?

Meanwhile, Roman and Boicourt are launching ScanFish. Yellow on top, orange on its belly with fins of black, it shoots 256 light beams into the water to see what's where. Its front bears a flame decal that Boicourt's staff pasted on a few years ago when he turned fifty-six. It's not Boicourt's shift but he's here anyway, making sure that all is well. He bows down slightly before ScanFish goes in the water, touching its flank.

Any underwater trip is fraught with risk. ScanFish is built to sense obstructions on the bottom and veer away from them, but there's so much to hit. The sea bed is strewn with wrecks and pieces of oil platforms damaged in hurricanes, not to mention thousands of buried pipelines. As well, I can see from a government navigational chart posted in the galley that the Gulf is littered with unexploded ordnances and dumping grounds for explosives.

The instrument goes in. We hold our breath.

All is well. It flies gently through the water, swooping evenly from the top to the bottom in elegant sinusoidal waves, collecting data.

Over on the other side of the *Pelican* it's a different story. Jochem and Lavrentyev have been up all night trying to get their new FlowCAM to work. No luck. They'd finally gone to sleep in the wee hours without resolving the problems. In scientific terms, this is high tragedy.

After dinner, there's still no luck. Jochem, so buoyant last night as he was setting up, is barely monosyllabic now. He's hunched over the recalcitrant computer, his brow black and furrowed.

Ludsin is trawling again. He's checked the nets thoroughly; the speed is perfect; the sea is as calm as it's possible to be; this system is working. Therefore, he figures, he should be able to catch some fish. He confides to me that he doesn't want millions of fish, just enough so that he can examine them later to see whether they're getting enough to eat—a ritual that demands that the creatures die. He hates to kill them and throws back as many as he can do without.

He throws the trawl in. Fifteen minutes later, he and his team are heaving in the nets. It's still 29 degrees and their faces gleam with sweat as they labour to land the fishing contraption. And then ... nothing. The nets are empty. 'There's no fricking fish,' he mutters.

It's near midnight, the end of my shift. Jochem has finally got some pictures, even if they're not the clear, coloured ones he was looking for. I wander past him and out onto the deck. The hot air packs the wallop of a fist after our air-conditioned lab.

We've been on hurricane watch today; a big one, Chris, has just broken up over Cuba and we're waiting to see whether it will pick up some of the unnaturally hot water from the Gulf and gather speed again. It's near the first anniversary of Hurricane Katrina and this whole part of the world is on high alert.

Surrounding the *Pelican* is a city of oil derricks, shining in the humid night for kilometres around, pumping oil and gas from beneath the sea floor. The Gulf produces roughly a third of the oil and a fifth of the gas for the US. Some of those petroleum products will be used to produce the fertilisers that farmers up the Mississippi are using to grow their crops and that, in turn, will feed this dead zone. Some will be used for fuel. All of it will produce the greenhouse gases that are contributing to global climate change with its warmer oceans, growing expanses of dead zones and higher intensity of hurricanes.

One of Ludsin's graduate students comes out on deck and looks over the side of the ship. He points. There, in the ship's light, we can see a couple of dozen small fish swimming alongside. We gasp with delight—this is the first tangible sign we've had that there is life in this part of the ocean.

The next day there's a squall, the residue of Hurricane Chris. We pull in all the instruments and wait it out. The sky is purplish black and the clouds are leaden.

Some of the team has been battling seasickness since we set out and this weather makes it worse. It's one of the great topics of discussion on board: ginger versus Dramamine versus wrist zappers. Everyone is trading war stories about the worst stomachs ever and the longest recovery time. It's not easy for most human beings to be on the open ocean.

One of Boicourt's lab technicians has been green and horizontal since she arrived. Today will be a rough day for her.

By night-time we've moved on and so has the worst of the gale. It's still raining torrentially and there's lightning and thunder, but we're in water that has oxygen now, just above the dividing line of 2 milligrams per litre.

At 11 p.m. Ludsin loads up the trawl and sinks it to the bottom. Water is pouring off his hard hat and yellow raincoat, and the deck is treacherous. Earlier this year, another ship he was aboard had been hit by lightning. He's a little wary.

When the trawl comes up, it's so full that it takes a winch to get it on deck. The relief is palpable, and so is the excitement. The men gather on deck—scientists, lab technicians and crew alike— heedless of the rain and lightning, eager to see. This exultation in the big catch is an ancient, primal joy, and one that must have touched fishermen throughout time.

It's mainly spot and croaker, two common Gulf fish—a total of seven species. Ludsin and his team are weighing them with a hand-held scale, faces scarlet with exertion. Sixty-two kilograms of spot and 113 kilograms of croaker. Ludsin's green shorts are soaked, his hair and glasses drenched.

'That's a lot of freakin' fish,' he says, a huge smile breaking out across his face.

We bag some samples of the fish for the freezer, labelling them carefully so he can examine them in greater detail back in Michigan.

By 12:30 Ludsin is standing at his computer again, absorbed in plotting the coordinates of the next route. Fish scales—trans- lucent, iridescent—fall from his hands as he types.

The fourth day at sea is marked by another tragedy. The cable connecting one of Jochem's instruments to the ship has snapped, and the instrument is lost at sea. Ludsin is on the run, out to the deck. By the time I get there, a ring of five men is huddled around the hand winch, mouths set in a straight line, silent. It feels like a hospital room where the doctors have lost a patient they thought they could save. There is sorrow, grief, maybe resignation that the perils of ocean study sometimes lead to this.

The sunset sky is lit by the burn of a huge natural gas flare from one of the petroleum rigs off to the side. On the other side, a rainbow.

Roman shakes his head and turns to me. 'Everything you put over the edge is expendable,' he says.

Now the men converge around Ludsin, the chief scientist, who will have to decide whether anything is to be done.

Jochem and Lavrentyev face him, arms crossed, legs set wide, talking earnestly. But it's no use: the *Pelican* can't turn back. Ludsin figures it would take two days to find the instrument at the cost of $6000 a day to run the boat, plus all the lost research time. The instrument is only worth $15,000. He has to put the expedition's success ahead of the loss of one instrument.

Jochem and Lavrentyev talk with each other for a while. Then they root around a bit and find some unused dumbbell weights on the lower deck of the ship. Somehow they rig up a proxy for the instrument they've lost so they can keep pumping surface water into their machine, collecting their bits of information.

About halfway through the cruise, the order is beginning to fray slightly. Lots of cruises last for five or six days; some only two or three. Ours, at eleven days, is stretching the limits of human nature. I've read about trips that went on for weeks or months and wonder how the scientists managed.

On this trip, most of the scientists and their teams are on two four-hour shifts a day. When you include the time it takes to get meals in the galley (at the universally fixed shipboard times of 6 a.m., noon and 6 p.m.), it means everybody's sleep is broken up into three- or four-hour chunks. In our four-person cabin deep in the hold, we're all on different shifts, so we keep waking each other up inadvertently when we stumble into bed in the dark. Ludsin is the anomaly: no one can figure out when he sleeps.

Add the general sleep deprivation to the repetitive tasks, no email, no phones, exceedingly close quarters, no privacy and an absolute prohibition on alcohol, and you have the makings of some short tempers.

For many of the men the crankiness plays out in the area of food. Food becomes absurdly important on a cruise. Many scientific ships pay as much attention to the care and nurturing of the chef as they do to the chief engineer. The *Pelican*, alas, is having a touch of trouble in the chef department right now and ours on this expedition is a last-minute fill-in who's never worked with this group before. He's here on sufferance.

To me, he's a marvel who has no trouble throwing together a fresh and inventive meal for twenty-plus people. But to some of the *Pelican*'s crew, he's a disaster who cooks the wrong things and sometimes commits the shipboard sin of putting lunch on the galley table five minutes later than the schedule says he should.

So now the captain has ordered the chef to pull out the ship's deep-fryer and use it. The men haven't been getting their quotient of fried foods and it's become a rallying cry of discontent. The galley—which is the only public space on the ship and where we eat, watch television and read if we can—is filled with greasy smoke.

Roman, the ship's storyteller, has seen it all before. On some cruises the no-alcohol rule flushes out the closet alcoholics who are forced to go cold turkey—then the fried food becomes a salve for the detoxifying liver. Roman remembers one fellow from years before who used to change personality and lose about 9 kilograms as he dried out on each year's cruise.

Roman, who's had his PhD for more than thirty years and is the director of the Horn Point Laboratory, has the long view.

And not just on shipboard politics—on the science, too. He's seen the science of the ocean change dramatically in his career span alone.

As he explains to me while we monitor ScanFish as it flies through the dead zone, until fairly recently scientists only understood what was in the water from what they could catch in nets. And the main reasons they studied the ocean were, first, to make a catalogue of what was there and, second, to make sure fishermen could keep catching it. It was an economic motivation more than a biological one. I remember that Ludsin's former organisation, the National Oceanic and Atmospheric Administration, is part of the US Department of Commerce and it starts to make sense.

For example, as Roman explains, the early interest in the El Niño weather patterns developed because those patterns affected the fishery. Early study of plankton came from the same motive: if you could understand when and where the plankton were plentiful, then you would know where the fish would be.

Then there were all the military reasons for trying to understand the ocean. The US Government poured money into ocean research during World War II so that the generals and admirals could understand currents for warfare purposes and retrieve military secrets on both sides from sunken submarines. It was the main reason governments supported research into submersibles.

That means that, until recently, there was little scientific work that pulled together all the pieces of today's ocean system, and even less that looked at how it compared with past or future ocean systems. No one knew that might be important. There was no reason to put the present into a context. And there weren't the tools—taking ice cores, for example—to reconstruct the earth's past environment or predict what could happen in the future.

So it seems that the switch in the ocean system is also causing a switch in the way ocean scientists are thinking. All of a sudden it's become critical to look at the past and the future in order to measure change in the system.

How is the concentration of carbon dioxide in the atmosphere affecting the ocean? I ask Roman.

The surprise is pH, he says. As the ocean absorbs extra carbon dioxide from the atmosphere, its reading moves from the base side of the scale toward the acid side through a fairly simple chemical reaction. The temperature of the global ocean is also on the rise. The physical structure—meaning, the system of currents—appears to be shifting and that means a change in who lives where. All of this affects the food webs in the ocean, which is part of what we're studying in microcosm here in the Gulf. Scientists don't yet know the trigger points that would push the ocean into a new regime where change would happen exponentially rather than gradually. And what of plankton, I ask. Will this vast ocean change so dramatically that plankton, the source of half the planet's oxygen, can't survive?

Roman chuckles a little. Plankton, some with calcium shells, some covered in silica and others naked, are among the planet's most adaptable creatures. They are known to live in waters as cold as 2 degrees Celsius and as hot as 45 degrees Celsius. There will always be plankton in the sea, he says.

I wander across the ship to the lab where Jochem is working. He gained his PhD in 1990 in the great German oceanographic centre of Kiel University and worked there for seven years as a research scientist before coming to North America. He's a different generation from Roman, yet he too has seen vast changes in the science.

He loves the tiniest plankton, called microplankton. Now that their machine is working properly he and Lavrentyev, who studied in Russia, have been telling me passionate tales about the beauty and diversity of microplankton shapes, about their colours and their sneaky strategies to stay alive, which remind me of an intricate war game.

Some of the plankton are both plants and animals at the same time, able to switch back and forth as needed. Some hunt and chase their food. Some are equipped with needle-like appendages that can puncture a hole in other plankton and suck out all the cytoplasm for food. Others build fortresses around themselves using sand particles they capture from the sea. They glue them together and then attach spines from other microscopic creatures to create an impenetrable ball.

When Jochem wanted to study these tiny plankton, even some of the giants in his field said they weren't worth studying. It was a struggle for him to persuade them that he should do his graduate work on them.

Today that attitude is changing, Jochem says. But the science on microplankton is still young. Scientists have only begun to examine the who's who in this planktonic world, and are not really looking at which plankton is doing what. Yet these creatures are at the base both of the ocean's food chain and of the chemistry of earth's atmosphere. One type of microplankton—cyanobacteria or blue-green algae—are the first creatures known to have existed on the planet and have been found in fossils from 3.5 billion years ago.

Cyanobacteria are the source of the planet's first big pulse of oxygen, the original photosynthesisers. Life as we know it could not exist without oxygen, as our study in the Gulf is showing. Which means that these tiny plankton have shaped the very development of all life on the planet. And, of course, as they photosynthesise, turning the energy of the sun into food and giving off oxygen, they also absorb carbon dioxide from the atmosphere and store it in the ocean, one of the planet's main mechanisms for removing carbon from the atmosphere. In other words, the planet's carbon cycle—and, therefore, its climate system—works through plankton.

Just how will these plankton be affected by the oceanic shifts brought on by climate change? It's a big discussion, Jochem tells me, and no one is sure, although it's plain that plankton have adapted to the cycles of the planet and the climate many times through the ages.

One of his concerns is that higher water temperatures might mean less mixing of deep, nutritious waters with the higher levels where the plankton need to live in order to catch the sun's rays. In other words, the plankton may be cut off from all the minerals and food they need to reproduce. (Of course, the opposite could happen and the plankton might go into overdrive, as they have in the California current.) If that happens, Jochem believes it will be the very tiny-celled phytoplankton that will thrive, because smaller plankton have more surface area compared to volume and it's the surface that absorbs the food—in other words, they can survive more handily than larger plankton can in water that has fewer nutrients. But that has implications for the productivity of the whole ocean. It takes about 45 kilograms of phytoplankton to make about 5 kilograms of copepods, which in turn make one pound of fish. When the plankton get smaller, more steps are needed to convert the energy of plankton to the energy of fish. That means fewer fish.

He shrugs. It's all quite speculative, he tells me. No one is really sure what the plankton will do.

Stu Ludsin is baffled. He keeps trawling. He keeps getting nothing. One of the other scientists jokes that they're trawling for water. The thing is, in the dead zone of Lake Erie, where Ludsin has also done a great deal of study and trawling, he finds that the fish collect on the edges of the zone and above it. That's what he's expected here in the Gulf. Instead, the fish appear simply to flee the whole area. He calls it 'bugging out', a reference to the emergency survival measure of evacuation.

Ludsin's acoustic device is showing a green water column, meaning that something is there, as opposed to a blue column, which means there's nothing. He stands in front of the screen, hard hat on, life vest, shorts and Wellingtons. 'What's the green?' he keeps asking. Is there any life down there? It remains a mystery.

Tonight is the full moon and that, combined with a generalised zombie-like state caused by sleep deprivation, is making everyone a little loony. We're drawn to the deck, paying homage to the heavy, bright moon, posing for pictures in front of it.

Roman begins calling Ludsin 'Ahab', after the single-minded captain in Herman Melville's novel who keeps trying to capture the elusive white-backed whale Moby Dick. Then somebody mockingly suggests that we extend the cruise for another week so we can trawl some more.

Things are a bit out of control. We've been cooped up too long and those narrow bunk beds we will be heading to after this shift are starting to feel like coffins. Last night I shone a torch onto the bottom of the bunk just centimetres above mine and found some desperate, inchoate words carved into the plywood—ghost messages from an earlier cruise.

What we don't talk about here on deck is that these scientists love the wonder of it all. Science is supposed to be about solving mysteries, answering questions, making order out of messiness. That's the scientific way. It is, as the great physicist Richard Feynman said, about the pleasure of finding things out.

Yet tonight, giddy under the power of this ancient moon, it seems that we are giving a tip of the hat to the larger order, the unknowable one: the great, plastic, endlessly creative nature that will instinctually find a new balance when the old balance is shot.

It's exhilarating for me to stand here, between what's known and what's not, and to see that, try as we might, we may never understand either the old balance or the new. In addition to our ravenous quest for answers, there's a quiet chuckle over the fact that we may never solve all these opaque planetary riddles; that we may only ever succeed in getting a glimpse of what the true questions are.

We abandon the moon, cram ourselves back into the airless ship and seek our berths for a few hours of restless sleep. Alas for Ludsin, the name Ahab sticks.

Oxygen at last. We've moved to a different part of the Gulf, outside the dead zone, and by 1 p.m. the oxygen has hit 3 milligrams per litre. Ludsin throws his trawl to the bottom and comes up with fish. Lots and lots of fish. Their mouths and gills open wide and settle into the rigid grin of death. They produce copious amounts of slime as they struggle to hold onto life.

'Oxygen, fish,' says Roman. 'Works every time.'

One of the bottom trawls today catches twenty-five different species. Ludsin's graduate students—who seem to need little sleep but tens of thousands of calories of food every day—happily identify the fish with reference books and bag the catch, sprinting to the top deck to throw the sealed plastic bags into Ludsin's chest freezer. Along with Boicourt's lab technician, who has rebounded from her terrible seasickness, they are the only ones who seem to have energy.

Ludsin tells me that the big test will come tomorrow, when he trawls in a different part of the water column where there's oxygen. That, he says, will show conclusively that the nets are working. So far, the mid-water trawls haven't come up with much.

By 7 p.m. we're so close to one of the oil rigs that our mobile phones can hook into their aerial signal. Everyone floods to the upper deck, phones in hand, eager to take up their real lives for a few minutes. My hands tremble as I punch in the numbers that will let me talk to my children and husband.

It's peaceful, hot, wondrous up here on the top deck. As I talk to my son, I see dolphins leaping on either side of the *Pelican*. This doesn't feel like the blob we've been cataloguing. Here, outside of the dead zone, there is life.

ScanFish is saved by a miracle.

Boicourt, unaccountably anxious over the instrument in the early hours of this morning, happened to notice that three of four screws holding a critical plate were gone.

The fourth was hanging by a thread. This is the plate that holds the cable to the instrument. Had the fourth screw failed, the ScanFish would have been lost to the deeps on its next dive. By the time Roman and I show up for our first shift he's screwed the plate back in place and we go out to inspect the repair.

ScanFish is one of about three such instruments in use in the US and so old now that it would be hard to replace—that's if the lab could find more than $100,000 to buy a new one.

'We dodged a bullet there,' Boicourt says. He and Roman gingerly put ScanFish into the water. It's an act of faith. They rush back to the controls and the screens to see how it's doing. Perfect. Better than ever.

Even though he's been up since before 4 a.m., Boicourt waits until his assistant, Carol Derry, shows up for her shift at noon. He tells her of the narrow escape in blow-by-blow detail and she listens raptly, immersed in the tale.

Later they stand together on the deck, watching ScanFish fly under the water, arms gently around each other's waists, wordless, eyes fixed on the cable.

The Ahab phenomenon is holding and Ludsin is disconsolate. He's trawling in the middle of the water column where there looks to be oxygen, and still no fish. Just jellies. Again, he worries that the nets aren't working well. He's hoping the night trawls will be better.

Now it's near midnight and the next trawl is due to be put in the water in a few minutes. Ludsin is standing at his computer in his rubber boots, a huge stack of academic papers to one side. He's making notes on the draft of a student's master's thesis. He's pale and has dark shadows under his eyes.

When the trawl comes up it contains lots of trigger fish, a popular aquarium species. It's not what he was looking for, but it tells him that the net has the capacity to catch fish . . . if only the fish were there.

Finally we're heading back to dock at Cocodrie on a continuous tracking route that will take us two days and cut through part of the blob from one end to the other. The other routes have been small slices, tracking in and out of the dead zone and along its margins.

By this time Roman is looking like a younger version of the American actor Clint Eastwood, stubble covering his chin. Boicourt is immaculate, patrician as always. Ludsin just looks exhausted. He hasn't been on his bike much.

We're talking about a heretical idea, another key scientist's tactic that can sometimes help frame the right questions. Sure, there's a blob. It's big at 17,000 square kilometres and has doubled in size since it was first routinely measured in the mid-1980s. It's unmixable except by hurricanes. It seems to be devoid of large forms of life; the general panoply of life you'd expect in these waters—including bottom-living one-celled creatures—is also absent. We will find out later, from the trip's results, that the dead zone is completely devoid of fish and of the zooplankton they feed on. The zooplankton that remain are squeezed up into the warmer, light-filled waters near the surface, which still have oxygen. But there they can't hide from the fish, and their eggs sink into the zone and suffocate before they hatch. Even the one-celled protozoa—protists that are neither plants nor animals nor fungi—are reduced in the oxygen-less water.

Does it matter, though, in the grand scheme of things, whether it's there? Maybe it's just a biological black hole that comes and goes. Don't the fish just go to another part of the Gulf and carry on their merry way? In fact, so far, while fishermen have to move further out into the Gulf to make their catch, the value and tonnage of the catch itself hasn't changed that much since the 1970s, when this blob first began to form with its current tenacity.

Roman has done a lot of work in the dead zone of Chesapeake Bay off the northeast coast of the US. It's clear there that the blob has had a hand in wiping out the sturgeons and diminishing the oysters by taking away the living space they need to spawn and live. And it's definitely had long-term adverse effects on the environment. Studies in other parts of the world, including in the Baltic, Black and Kattegat seas, have shown that the dead zones have destroyed fisheries entirely or caused them to crash.

As for the Gulf? Is it a signal of much worse things to come, particularly as the climate keeps changing and the fertilisers—now ironically being used even more to grow corn for biodiesel fuels in a bid to slow down greenhouse gas emissions—keep flowing down the Mississippi? What will the future bring? And how does it connect, if at all, with the great oxygen starvation that happened in the ocean at the time of the Great Dying 250 million years ago?

Ludsin reminds me that ours is the first study to look at the whole column of water in this dead zone rather than just the underside of the blob on the floor of the Gulf. All we know for sure is that historical fishing grounds are barren during much of the year here, that the essential nature of a living resource has changed.

Nancy Rabalais is the marine scientist at the Louisiana Universities Marine Consortium in Cocodrie who discovered the Gulf's dead zone in the mid-1980s and has tracked it every year since. She's known as the 'Queen of the Dead Zone' in the popular press and has been pilloried by farmers throughout the US for fingering their fertilisers as the cause of the blob. For years she was a voice in the wilderness in the scientific world for her work on this phenomenon.

'It was sort of like acid rain in the beginning. Nobody believed it,' she told me in Cocodrie before we set sail.

Now, her work has spawned all sorts of other studies, including this cruise and a multilevel government task force recommending voluntary measures upstream so that the blob shrinks in size to no more than 5000 square kilometres.

It's a far-off dream.

Even if the plankton-feeding nitrogen and phosphorus were cut down, no one is certain that life in the dead part of the Gulf would return. There are dozens of scientific papers she and others have written on the dead zone in the Gulf; I've been reading them between ScanFish watches. They report that when the former Soviet bloc collapsed and subsidies for fertilisers dropped through the 1990s, the nitrogen flowing into the Black Sea also fell. By 1999 the Black Sea's dead zone had receded dramatically—but the plankton and fish didn't come back. Nor did they return in the Bodden inlets off the Baltic Sea.

It turns out that the soil acts as a sponge for synthetic nitrogen, and possibly has for decades. A UK study on experimental plots of land showed that they continued to leak significant amounts of nitrogen forty years after it had stopped being applied to the soil. In Sweden, nitrogen kept leaching into the water for thirteen years after fertilisation had stopped and in amounts that, strangely, did not diminish. So even if the nitrogen eventually washes out and the oxygen comes back, the original mix of life in the former dead zones may not return. As Rabalais says in one of her papers, they may have developed a new, different normal, one that only lightly resembles what was there before.

Rabalais has also come to be concerned that humans could be shifting the global nitrogen cycle through the use of synthetic nitrogen in agriculture. If that is so, what effect will that have on the global ocean systems?

The answers are as yet unclear.

By midnight the constraints of this long trip are loosening. A bunch of the men are gathered in the galley having a monster game of poker, betting with mini chocolate bars. It's the first time this trip I've seen Ludsin sit down. His feet are up and he's eating ice cream out of the tub.

We're almost back to shore and it's my last shift on ScanFish. Roman lets me track it on my own for a few minutes while he runs off to do something else. When he comes back, he gives me a high-five. 'You flew solo!' he says, grinning.

Then, Cocodrie and firm land appear. I jump off the *Pelican*, legs wobbly, breathing in the earth and trees. The scientific team has been packing up for hours and now all those kilograms of equipment and samples, containing millions of pieces of new data, need to be shifted off the boat and into vans, trailers and boxes to be posted home.

Ludsin loads the chest freezer into his U-Haul and gets behind the wheel of his van. The freezer is carrying hundreds of kilograms of fish, hard caught, and he's got an eighteen-hour drive to Michigan ahead of him before he can plug it in again. It will take the scientists years to figure out the meaning of all they've just gathered.

As for me, I have a longing to understand part of the ocean's chemistry that this crowd hasn't been looking at: pH. So I track down two of the world's experts and fly to Puerto Rico to meet them at a scientific conference.

CHAPTER 3

READING THE VITAL SIGNS: PH

Puerto Rico: When the seas turn to acid

Every single chemical reaction that makes up the chemistry of life occurs in water. Water, the universal solvent, dissolves almost anything, including gold.

Chemically, water is made up of two hydrogen atoms and a single atom of oxygen. Together they make the most abundant molecule on the planet. And one of the defining chemical characteristics of water is its pH reading. Pure water at room temperature has a pH of 7. Above that level, the water is basic; below, acidic.

A key characteristic of salty water in the open ocean is that its pH has remained at 8.2 for millions of years, and that level is tied to the concentration of carbon dioxide in the atmosphere.

In fact, ocean water pH is hard to change. The ocean system is set up to make sure its chemistry doesn't change too much and so it takes something cataclysmic to do so. If it does change, there are elaborate systems in place to return it to normal, mainly through the weathering of rocks from land. The creatures that live in the ocean are extremely sensitive to pH and they don't thrive when ocean chemistry shifts around.

When masses of carbon dioxide gas enter the atmosphere through slow planetary processes such as tectonic plate shifting or biological activity, the ocean pH isn't very sensitive. It holds its own. Slow, in scientific terms, means over the span of about one million years or more.

If, on the other hand, carbon dioxide gas goes into the atmosphere quickly, the ocean pH can't hold fast, and falls. Quickly, in this context, means in 10,000 years or less.

Ken Caldeira and Michael Wickett, deep-time earth systems modellers at California's Lawrence Livermore National Laboratory, are extremely good at explaining this, and did so in their 2003 paper in the scientific journal *Nature*. But they were curious about the pace of the increase in carbon dioxide concentrations in today's atmosphere compared to what had happened over the past 300 million years. So they ran some models. They calculated that if humans keep burning fossil fuels at the rate we have been for past decades, until we burn up the last of them in centuries to come, the ocean's pH will fall by 0.7 of a unit because the infusion of carbon dioxide would be extremely rapid, in geological terms. However, geological records show that the ocean's pH has never dropped more than 0.6 of a unit over the past 300 million years, with the possible exception of some 'rare and catastrophic events in earth's history'.

The ocean's pH, it seems, is not something to trifle with.

Joanie Kleypas and Chris Langdon know this to their cost. We are at the end of a ground-breaking scientific meeting in Puerto Rico and we have finally found a few hours to talk.

Still, Kleypas, a scientist at the National Center for Atmospheric Research in Boulder, Colorado, and Langdon, who is at the University of Miami, are slightly wary as we sit down together, in the way that scientists who are delivering profoundly unpopular findings can sometimes be. It's not that they don't trust the information they're about to explain; it's that they have been so thoroughly spanked by other scientists whenever they try to say what they've been finding. It is outside the canon.

This morning was a case in point. Kleypas and Langdon made a pithy presentation to the other scientists at this conference, in a bid to convince them that a new monitoring machine being installed on the coral reef in the bay in front of our hotel ought to capture information that would describe the pH of the water and how the corals are responding to it.

It was a hard sell, followed by harsh questions, even from this intimate group. A much harder sell, for example, than the pitch from a fish biologist to install an acoustic phone so that scientists could listen to the fish chatter and hope for clues about how healthy the coral reef is.

The heresy of Kleypas and Langdon is stating that carbon dioxide entering the atmosphere from burned fossil fuels is affecting the global ocean's acidity and, therefore, the proportion of carbonate ions in the water. In turn, the proportion of carbonate ions affects the ability of creatures to use the sea water's calcium for their shells and skeletons.

Further, they say that by the time the carbon dioxide concentration in the atmosphere has reached double its pre-industrial level (from 280 to 560 parts per million)—which could easily happen by the middle of this century—marine organisms will have access to 30 per cent less calcium than they once had.

By the time of tripling, it will be just half.

It's a doomsday scenario for the corals, some shelled plankton and many other creatures that depend on calcium to live—they're known as calcifiers—because at some point they won't be able to build their shells and skeletons.

Eventually, when the seas become acidic enough and the carbonate ion concentration drops low enough, these creatures' calcium shells and skeletons will simply dissolve.

Kleypas remembers when she first realised how serious the pH issue is. She was in a meeting with Langdon in Boston in 1998. This was a scientific committee on ocean research, made up of academics affiliated with the Society for Integrative and Comparative Biology, once known as the American Zoological Society.

This group was talking about carbon dioxide and how it affects the concentration of carbonate ions in the ocean, a topic so arcane and seemingly irrelevant that, Kleypas remembers, they hadn't even learned it at university. It certainly wasn't on the scientific radar.

Nevertheless, this group pooled their information and did some back-of-envelope calculations. That's when they realised how low the carbonate ion concentration would fall if carbon dioxide concentrations in the atmosphere keep rising. Then they realised that they were looking at a marine Armageddon.

Kleypas ran into the bathroom outside the committee room and threw up.

'It's pretty serious when you're messing around with calcifiers,' she says, adding that the fossil record shows that when carbonate saturation falls, some creatures that need calcium become extinct.

Would humans survive if coral reefs and shelled plankton and other sea creatures that need shells become extinct? How much of a life support system are they for us?

Plankton produce half the oxygen in the atmosphere and are at the base of the planet's largest food chain. When they make their calcium-based shells they're storing carbon in the ocean, keeping it out of the atmospheric system. (Not all plankton make calcium shells. Some have no shells and others make theirs of silica.)

We have no idea what other life forms that we depend on would vanish if plankton died out. And we still don't know to what degree humans are symbionts with all these creatures we are endangering.

That means Kleypas and the others who are working on this issue of ocean chemistry have unwittingly embarked on the ultimate human quest: to find out not where we came from but where we are going. It is the great end point of human imagination.

A year later those off-handed Boston calculations became a major article in the journal *Science*, one of the bibles of the scientific world. They received a lot of press coverage and drew a chorus of outrage from fellow scientists who questioned everything about the premise, from the chemistry to the calculations to the assumptions. It reminds me of the accusations surrounding the findings of Copernicus, Galileo and Darwin.

The ocean, the critics contended, is too robust, too massive, to be affected by human actions. It has back-up systems for its back-up systems.

They called for more investigation and more analysis, including examination of other eras in the earth's history when ocean chemistry has changed rapidly. All subsequent research has backed up Kleypas, Langdon and the others.

So what does all this really mean? Why is it important enough that a top scientist would vomit when she figured it out? It's because she understood the ineluctable poetry of chemistry. In plain language, it means that when we pump carbon dioxide from the oil, gas and coal that we burn into the atmosphere, it also enters the ocean.

The two media of life on the planet—air and water—exchange gases across the vast surface of the ocean exactly where the water molecules meet those of the air. It's a continuous, two-way process that is key to the earth's ability to support life as we know it.

So as we add carbon dioxide to the atmosphere, this gas exchange alters the fundamental chemistry of the ocean. That's in addition to changing the climate—a separate and also severe problem.

When you add up all the carbon dioxide that cutting down trees and burning fossilised carbon has put into the atmosphere, roughly a third has ended up in the ocean, a third is still in the air and a third has been reabsorbed into the land. And while carbon dioxide acts like a giant blanket in the atmosphere, trapping heat over the planet, it remains chemically boring. It's not reacting with anything. It's just hanging there, intact, making up an ever greater proportion of the air.

Today, that proportion is roughly 387 parts per million by volume, compared to about 280 before industrialisation began. It's increasing exponentially each year and is expected to reach 560, or double pre-industrial levels, by about 2065. There's no scientific reason to believe that the level has risen above 300 at any time in the past twenty million years.

There's already so much human-generated carbon dioxide in the ocean that scientists have tracked it, with its unique chemical markers, to the depth of 1000 metres. In the cold and restless North Atlantic, where waters churn in a great, deep conveyor belt, scientists can measure the human carbon fingerprint at 3000 metres.

This is an almost unimaginable amount of carbon.

Carbon dioxide in the ocean is not inert as it is in the atmosphere. It metamorphoses, some of it dissolving and interacting with other substances, including sea water. This produces a lot of electrically charged atoms and molecules known as ions. These ions have either gained electrons, meaning they are negatively charged, or lost them, meaning they are positive. Like magnets, these charged atoms either repel or attract other ions, leading to chemical reactions.

Carbon dioxide added to sea water produces positive hydrogen ions plus several negatively charged forms of dissolved carbon which include the carbonate ion—the one that Kleypas is so concerned about—and bicarbonate. The more carbon dioxide the ocean absorbs, the more chemical reaction occurs. And the more chemical reaction, the more positive hydrogen ions. The more hydrogen ions, the lower the pH. In other words, the more carbon dioxide the ocean absorbs, the more acidic the ocean becomes.

So far, surface ocean pH has dropped by a little more than a tenth of a pH unit, from about 8.2 to about 8.05, meaning that it is still slightly basic. This drop may not seem to be significant, but it is huge in terms of how it affects biology due to the logarithmic pH scale. The plants, animals and bacteria that live in the ocean have evolved to thrive in a chemical mixture that stays within a certain range.

Sitting in the tropical heat of southern Puerto Rico, Langdon tells me about two cruises that ran from Antarctica to Iceland, stopping every 48 kilometres, or half degree of latitude, to check pH. One cruise took place in 1991 and the other, 2005. Even within that time, surface water pH had dropped.

Again, it's helpful to think of the human body. The pH of arterial blood in humans has to be in the range of 7.35 to 7.45. If it goes higher or lower than that we get very sick and could die. Already, ocean pH has dropped by an amount larger than the whole range of healthy pH in the human body. And it's still changing as the carbon dioxide load in the atmosphere keeps increasing. Despite political attempts around the world to lower emissions, emissions are actually rising more quickly now than they have at any time since we started measuring. A paper published in late 2007 found that global emissions from fossil fuels and cement making were more than a third higher in 2006 than they had been in 1990.

Earlier this week, before we got mired in heresy and pH, Kleypas and I did some snorkelling on the coral reef here at La Parguera Natural Reserve. Because Puerto Rico is a territory of the United

States, this natural reserve is part of the American network of protected marine areas. Its main attraction is a bay that lights up the dark with the natural fluorescence of marine life. It's become an international tourist draw for the Caribbean. More than that, though, this reserve has a lot of the ocean living spaces that characterise the tropics, and all in close, researchable quarters.

Among them are the complex-rooted mangroves that can turn sea into land. Because life collects at these margins where different living spaces collide, mangroves are extraordinarily rich, feeding and sheltering creatures that depend on air and water as well as land. Some of the mangroves are making tiny islands, the promise of new earth to come. There are wide beds of sea grasses, the plants whose ancestors made the leap from ocean to land and then went back to the ocean again, as well as vibrant shorelines, ponds crusted with salt and flat plains thick with the larger algae.

The reserve is also home to a Caribbean coral reef that forms protective rings along the outside of this calm bay beyond our hotel. Just outside the reef, the island's placid shelf drops abruptly to several thousand metres, opening up to the mysteries of the deeps. At the heart of the whole reserve is the University of Puerto Rico's Magueyes Island Laboratory, a short boat ride from our hotel.

We took a boat out to part of the reef where technicians and scientists were struggling to put up the monitoring tower that would provide a continuous stream of information about the sea. It was the third of these that the US Government had set up and more were planned in other parts of the ocean in the months ahead. The think-tank we were taking part in was aimed at advising the government about what information ought to be collected.

I wondered why there hadn't been data collecting before this. Hadn't there been enough evidence of change to warrant at least looking at the numbers?

So much of the sea is invisible, on some level a notional place rather than a real one, that it's been easy for humans to ignore.

And it's now up to those like Kleypas and Langdon, who have figured out what's really happening, to make its watery darkness visible to the rest of us. Snorkelling in this protected place, I thought of the arc of human knowledge about the ocean over time. It is like the pH scale, growing slowly at the beginning and expanding exponentially in recent years.

As far as scientists have been able to piece together, humans first settled by the sea only about 164,000 years ago, a mere blink of the eye given the 4.5-billion-year history of the planet. The evidence comes from a recent archaeological find in a cave at Pinnacle Point on the South African cape filled with the remains of cooked shellfish. Scientists concluded that those early sea-dwelling humans were using the colour ochre, an important sign that they were capable of abstract thought, a leap forwards in human evolution.

Many evolutionary biologists have theorised that humans were able to develop intellectually and travel so far from our African birthplace because we found seafood, with its high fat content—the perfect brain food. That means we can draw a direct line between the sea's riches and what humans are today. In terms of nutrition and transport—not to mention climate and oxygen—human civilisation and the sea are intimately connected. Until those ancient African ancestors settled on a cape beach, our species—which evolved only about 200,000 years ago and is a latecomer to the planet—knew the plains and the jungles but not the vast ocean or its shores.

Those early humans who glimpsed the ocean off the cape could have had no concept that water covers nearly three-quarters of the surface of the planet. They could not have known that the ocean was the cradle of life or that humans develop in the salty water of the womb with gill arches and gill slits that later develop into parts of the ear. They could not have seen the ocean as an integral part of the carbon and oxygen cycles, or even have known that such cycles existed. Still less might they have imagined that life as they knew it was dependent on the sea staying healthy and stable.

Even much later, in the relatively recent history of modern civilisation when the Mesopotamians started describing our planet for posterity, they imagined a flat disc bathed by a salty body of water. To these thinkers, the planet was all about land. Indeed, the English name for our planet, earth, comes from the Anglo-Saxon word for soil or land.

The idea that the planet was mainly land has persisted. The first, highly metaphoric maps of the world show land taking up most of the surface of the globe. The marvellous maps of Ptolemy, who lived in the second century, show a preponderance of land and little water. In his day, as throughout much of human history, the intellectual quest was to figure out how that land-planet interacted with the heavens, certainly not how land, air and sea were conjoined.

In fact, it was thought that the stars controlled the destiny of individuals, societies, even empires, if only they could be decoded. The heavens—or their rulers, the gods—decided the fates of us all, even intervening in human affairs on occasion, punishing the wicked and rewarding the good.

By the early medieval ages, mapmakers put Jerusalem at the physical centre of the planet. Land masses still covered the bulk of the surface, with tiny rivulets marking the rivers and seas as if they were watery roads. And while there were inklings by the sixteenth century that the planet was mainly water, the sea was still largely seen as a two-dimensional entity—key to transport, military might and trade dominance. The sea might have provided fish and other food, but it was mostly for sailing on to get to other places, for bending to the will of man.

The seas were named after the lands they abutted. We even named many sea creatures—like the sea horse, the swordfish, the sea cow and the cat fish—by names that liken them to creatures and goods on land. The immense third dimension of the ocean—the vast deeps that give it its biological importance on the planet—was still unimagined.

When humans finally began to explore those depths systematically in the eighteenth and nineteenth centuries, it was mainly to make sure that shipping was safer. It was 1876—when the *Challenger* with its British scientists sailed back home with their findings—before anyone knew that parts of the ocean floor were far deeper than anyone had imagined.

It was the 1930s before anyone physically went to the ocean's depths and the 1950s before it was more commonplace, and then the exploration was driven largely by the military to aid recovery of sunken ships and missiles, and to lay down cables.

It is a beautiful irony that humans have also been drawn to the depths so they can recover lost land treasure or artifacts of human life on land, such as the *Titanic*, many unaware that the ocean itself is the real treasure.

Jacques Cousteau was one of the early underwater scientific explorers, finding creatures that had never been seen before by diving with an air suit. It was 1951 before anyone knew how deep the ocean could go—10,923 metres in the Pacific Ocean's Mariana Trench, the oceanic inverse of Mount Everest—and 1960 before anyone got there.

Until quite recently biologists have thought of most of the ocean as a desert—and an immutable one at that—unaware that it teems with life even in its deeps. It's only in the past few generations that they have come to understand the importance of the ocean to life on the planet as a whole and realised that the ocean's life forms have changed dramatically since the beginning of time, in step with pulses of extinction and new creation. The idea that humans can change the ocean's very chemistry and its capacity to support life is newer still. That the ocean contains the switch of life, and that the human hand is on that switch, is on the frontier of scientific thought.

At La Parguera, where the technicians were installing the monitoring tower as Kleypas and I snorkelled, the reef was in poor shape. Just 20 per cent of the coral that ought to have been there was still alive. But it still had beauty and majesty. It was a good reef to experiment on, to see whether it was possible to put pieces back together once they had been destroyed.

Some researchers were trying to rear baby corals. Others were trying to seed a type of sea urchin, *Diadema*, which used to eat a lot of the algae that no other creature ate. Sort of like the bison on the North American plains, the urchins were the main grazers of the coral reef, keeping the algae in check so other animals and plants had room to grow.

In 1983, before most of the scientists even discovered the critical role the sea urchins played in keeping the balance of the reefs, the urchins disappeared mysteriously right across the Caribbean. And while they've started coming back at a glacial pace in the past few years, they are still too rare to keep the algae down. Thus, the attempts to seed them.

I put my arms at my sides, kicking against the waves, moving with the water, making progress toward the shore, eager to see what was there. Closer to shore, the reef was a graveyard. Only about 5 per cent was still alive. I kicked up against a type of *Acropora*, one of the branching corals that helped build this reef, and recoiled in case I was hurting it. When I went back to look, I saw it was dead. Just rubble.

There's a long list of hazards for corals in the Caribbean, and this is before the big effects from the changing ocean chemistry have kicked in. Over the past three decades, roughly 80 per cent of corals in the Caribbean have perished.

Some have died because the carbon dioxide we're pumping into the atmosphere is hiking the temperature of the water, killing the symbiotic algae that live inside the coral animals and feed them. Some are dead because there's too much fishing across the Caribbean, and this removes some of the creatures that can keep marine life balanced. Others have succumbed to the sewage and pesticides that wash down from humans on the land; some have been lost to the dust carrying fungal spores, disease and toxic chemicals that blows in from Africa in increasing amounts since the drought has set in there.

Some have fallen to a strange and virulent outbreak of coral diseases that have infected the Caribbean. With only 8 per cent of the world's coral reefs, the Caribbean is reporting 66 per cent of the world's coral disease events. Some corals are being sickened by four or five diseases at the same time. A leading theory is that the cumulative effects of all the environmental stress have left them unable to defend themselves against illnesses.

All in all, the corals here are dying faster than they can grow back, even in this protected area. The situation, as one of the coral scientists here has said, is not good.

It's almost as if the switch to a new system has already happened here. A new balance may be on its way, one that will reinforce itself rather than trying to re-create the old system.

Kleypas and I kept swimming. Finally we found an *Acropora* that was still alive. Just one, in a field of crumbling skeletons. It spread like the rack of an elk, brown, regal.

The interview at our parador is drawing to a close. The late afternoon sun is hot and clear, the ocean heartbreakingly blue, invisibly ill. Some of the other scientists from this conference are cavorting at the pool, kicking off the intellectual rigours of the past several days.

Kleypas and Langdon could probably talk about this for many more hours, but I'm spent. It feels as though the implications of what I've been hearing snake hundreds of thousands of years into a future that we can only try to imagine. I'm overwhelmed. We still have only pieces of this puzzle and they are showing us a picture that is terrifying.

How do these scientists on the front lines keep going? Langdon points to the great strides humans have made to stop acid rain and heal the Great Lakes; the banning of DDT sparked by Rachel Carson's book *Silent Spring*; the attempts to repair the ozone hole.

Kleypas has hope, too. But, like Langdon, she is an intelligent optimist, not a faith seeker. She has a place in Costa Rica, the fabled Central American country that has successfully based its economy on conservation rather than destruction. She stays there for part of each year.

The rainy season at the end of 2005 was unusually long and wet in Costa Rica for reasons unknown but possibly connected to global climate change. The jungle trees there don't flower until the rain ends. But the rain was so intense that many of the trees didn't bear fruit—the rain knocked off the flowers. That small change meant that as many as half the spider monkeys in the country's Corcovado National Park starved to death. At the end, the monkeys were so ravenous that they came down from the trees to scavenge for food—unsuccessfully—on the jungle floor.

Nobody had expected it. At first, biologists thought the monkeys were diseased, maybe with yellow fever. Finally they realised that the timing of the food cycle was off—not unlike what caused the deaths of the baby birds on the Great Barrier Reef that same year because the fish had moved to cooler waters. Or the unborn turtles at Mon Repos on the Australian coast that cooked in their own shells in the heat.

Kleypas's point is that we only feebly understand how some of these great earth systems work and the planet is capable of tossing us some big surprises.

In the ocean, we understand even less. We don't comprehend enough to know how great the risks are. In fact, the further along the logarithmic index of knowledge we get, the more we understand how little we know.

There are only a few places in the world where scientists are putting the theory of ocean acidification into practice. One is Plymouth in England, and I know this because I've run into some of their scientists in the course of my research. It seems critical to me as I leave Puerto Rico to go on to England and see what they're finding out. When I call them up, they're only too eager to show me around.

I check back with Kleypas in 2008—two years after our first meeting—to see whether the monitoring system at La Parguera is tracking seawater chemistry as she and Langdon had suggested. By that point they had done some testing of water off the reef and found that despite the poor state of the reef, they can still get a little information about how the reef is photosynthesising, breathing and forming calcium. There's only just enough of it left.

CHAPTER 4

READING THE VITAL SIGNS: METABOLISM

Plymouth, England: The fate of the plankton

Plankton are the nonchalant wanderers of the ocean. They go with the flow. And one of the toughest, least understood questions about the changing global ocean is where plankton will go next. 'Go' in the geographical sense as well as the evolutionary, biological, chemical and even metaphysical.

Does it matter where they go?

Resoundingly, yes. Impossible as it seems, this question—unimagined by most of us—may be the most important question humans will ever grapple with.

Plankton—a group of tiny organisms that range from microscopic marine viruses and bacteria to single-celled plants with fabulously ornate shells to minuscule plant-eating animals —are the lynchpin on which life itself depends. Not only do they produce half of the planet's oxygen but they are also responsible for a host of different, invisible and interlocked parts of the metabolism of the planet.

These aimless drifters nestle at the very bottom of the ocean's food chain and at the very top of the planet's life-giving chemical cycles of oxygen, nitrogen and carbon. It is fair to say that if plankton vanished tomorrow, the marine food chain would fall apart.

Despite their immense planetary significance, hardly anybody gives plankton a thought, even in the scientific community. One notable exception is the clutch of scientists who do rough-and-tumble plankton experiments at the marine institutions of Plymouth in southern England. The standing joke is that Plymouth has more marine biologists per square metre than anywhere else in the European Union. And, without question, Plymouth Sound is one of the best studied bits of ocean anywhere.

To begin with, Plymouth is home to the second oldest marine science organisation in the world: the Marine Biological Association of the United Kingdom, established in 1888. Seven of the association's scientists have captured Nobel prizes. The Sir Alister Hardy Foundation for Ocean Science is also here. Its scientists have been tracking plankton's wayfaring habits in the sea for more than seventy years using hand-tooled machines that rely on ancient watchmakers' techniques. It is the longest-running marine biology survey in the world.

As well, the seaside city boasts Plymouth Marine Laboratory, an internationally recognised research centre on marine topics. Rather than looking only at small pieces of the ocean's problems, the laboratory takes an unusually comprehensive view. Its aim is to examine plankton and other marine creatures—using techniques that include satellite imagery and computer models as well as hands-on experimentation—in order to assess the health of the planet itself. And the implications of any changes in its health. Its scientists are on the very cutting edge of understanding that the ocean is the planet's main life-support system and that it is changing in ways that humans urgently need to understand.

When I encounter several scientists from Plymouth Marine Laboratory at an international meeting in China I notice that they give by far the most bracing and forward-looking talks of the week-long event. If anyone can tell the full story of plankton, this crowd can.

So here I am in Plymouth. I've come to think of it as Plankton Central.

Because I'm dealing with plankton, which are so inscrutable, my path of research is not straightforward. It meanders from scientist to scientist, experiment to experiment. The only common thread is that the scientists and experiments are all in Plymouth.

The marine ecologist Melanie Austen leads a group of scientists doing experiments at the laboratory on ocean pH. Here, the changing acidity of the global ocean is not under discussion, as it was at the meeting in Puerto Rico—it's incontrovertible. In fact, many of these scientists have been responsible for teaching government leaders in the UK about what they call the 'other carbon dioxide problem' and helping to put it on the political map.

While Austen's group doesn't have any definitive findings on how plankton will respond to more acidic seas—that's still unsolved—they're getting clues from the creatures that live on and in the mud of Plymouth Sound.

The scientists start by re-creating the ocean in covered vats in their cavernous, frigid laboratory. Then they add cores of mud containing sea-bed animals. Finally, they pipe carbon dioxide into the air above the vats and then watch what happens to the acidity of the water and the animals living in it.

As Kleypas, Langdon and other scientists have worked out, the more carbon dioxide is pumped into the vats, the lower the pH goes. Many of the animals react catastrophically, while a few, such as some types of crabs and mussels, seem to be able to compensate for the lower pH, at least as adults. Those that don't compensate can't maintain their internal chemistry. The intimate processes of the cells—building proteins, using enzymes—stop working as they should.

In human medical terms it's akin to the diabetic whose blood sugar rises far too high. The chemistry of the blood is wrong, and that affects the heart, the nervous system, the circulation and other bodily functions.

One of Austen's team has shown me some photographs of the guts of sea urchins and brittle stars (relatives of starfish) that have tried to survive in the more acidic water. Their digestive systems have fallen into shreds.

At the same time, the urchins' and brittle stars' reproductive systems go slightly mad, producing genetic material with frenzied abandon in an attempt to create offspring before they die. It's a well-catalogued animal response to full-body stress. But, as Austen points out, baby urchins and brittle stars—more vulnerable than their parents to the increasing acidity—will die in their hostile new environment anyway. Plus, as the pH continues to fall, the animals' developing eggs start to break down, meaning that they would eventually stop reproducing at all.

This is the picture of an utter failure to thrive.

These animals are sea-bed engineers, working away in the mud and helping to control how quickly the food and minerals in that mud get recycled into the chain of life. A change in acidity affects not only the animal but also its function within the wider system.

This is obviously important for the animal's own survival, but it's also important because the same factors may affect plankton, not to mention countless other plants, animals, bacteria and viruses in the sea.

It's what Jerry Blackford, one of the people at the laboratory who runs computer models of ocean acidification, calls 'the disconnect'. He means that as the ocean's pH falls, the creatures that live in the ocean will be faced with a level of acidity that they and their ancestors have not experienced in millions of years. His models show that by 2050 the pH will be lower than it has been for twenty million years. The ocean's life forms will be disconnected from their own evolutionary heritage.

Blackford has been studying a plentiful, ancient plankton called coccolithophores. Known as coccoliths for short, these are one-celled marine plants that make complex plated armour for themselves out of calcium, carbon and oxygen that they absorb from the ocean. The white cliffs of Dover are made up of trillions upon trillions of these ancient microscopic plates.

Each species of coccolith—there have been about 4000 since they emerged in the Jurassic fossil record, and most of them are now extinct—makes a unique type of shell. Under the microscope some of the plates look like the lids of garbage cans, others like the leaves of an artichoke. Many resemble the petals of flowers, sculpted from limestone.

Like corals and a raft of other marine creatures, the coccoliths need calcium to make their armour. The more acidic the sea becomes, the less calcium is available for plates, reefs, shells and other calcium-needy structures.

How would a naked coccolith fare? That's uncertain, says Blackford. One possibility is that they would die off more easily from viruses and predators. But this could become a moot point: once atmospheric carbon dioxide gets to 1000 parts per million—it is now about 387—the models show that the number of coccoliths in the ocean crashes, whether they are naked or plated.

If the coccoliths can't make their plates because there's not enough calcium available in the sea water or because they can't be as numerous in acidic seas, they won't use up the carbon that they are now absorbing from the ocean and which, when they die, will be sent to the bottom of the ocean for thousands of years. These microscopic creatures, so tiny that a level teaspoon holds about 860,000 of them, are the prime mechanism for storing carbon in the deep ocean. In fact, when they evolved hundreds of millions of years ago, they revolutionised the regulation of ocean carbon chemistry. If they don't send all that carbon to the sea floor any more, how will the effects cascade through this fiendishly intricate ocean system?

Says Blackford, 'The first honest answer is that we don't know.'

I leave Blackford's office and wander along the shore of this port city. My cheeks turn scarlet in the sharp winter wind. The air carries the ancient scent of decaying fish and sea salt.

Plymouth Sound is one of the largest natural harbours in Europe and that has made it the opening act in the theatre of much Western history. Even today, the Royal Navy plays war games in the harbour once a week, on Thursdays, summoning war ships from distant points to practise manoeuvres.

This harbour launched Francis Drake's storied circling of the planet in the sixteenth century. In the seventeenth century, the pilgrims marched down the Plymouth steps and onto the *Mayflower* to make their home in the New World.

The following century James Cook set off from this harbour three times in a race to discover, map and claim the world. And in the nineteenth century, Charles Darwin caught a fair wind from here on board the *Beagle* for the five-year journey that would change how humans understood their origins and their place on earth.

Humans used to think the sea was a worthy foe to be conquered by seacraft so it could be used to get us to other places, including where the fish and other humans in ships were. Being able to triumph over the sea meant being able to conquer new lands, build empires, get rich and have mastery over hunger and domination by others.

Are we capable, now that we have a more sophisticated understanding of the meaning of the sea, of shifting this primal understanding of what it is for? And of understanding that we need now to protect it instead of believing we can force it into submission?

John Zachary Young, one of the most eminent biologists and neurophysicists of the twentieth century, published the definitive textbook *The Life of Vertebrates* in 1950. It is still a university staple. Young studied the rhythms of evolution, the great, rapid planetary spasms that created a lot of new species in a relatively short period of time. And not just the individual events or even the larger patterns, but also the underlying causes that determine the patterns. He investigated the workings of the systems that create and destroy new species, and sought to understand how to predict how those systems will work in the future.

Young writes: 'Too often in the past we have been content to accumulate unrelated facts. It is splendid to be aware of many details, but only by the synthesis of these can we obtain either adequate means for handling so many data or knowledge of the natures we are studying.

'In order to know life—what it is, what it has been, and what it will be—we must look beyond the details of individual lives and try to find rules governing all.'

This reasoning took Young to the ocean: 'The composition of the ocean is of special interest to biologists since life first became possible because of conditions in the sea, and then evolved there for perhaps [two billion years], that is to say for the greater part of its whole history.

'Living things still retain in their ionic make-up certain characteristics of the sea, indeed some authors have interpreted the blood plasma of vertebrates as a relic of the Palaeozoic sea.'

He's saying that the sea is the mother of life and that we carry her within us. We are connected in the most fundamental possible way with the global ocean that gave us life.

This is poetic, but it is also biologically significant. It means that the chemistry of the ocean over time has helped to determine what forms of life could come into being. The ocean, as Tim

Flannery explained on that dusky beach in Australia, holds not just the origin but also the fate of life.

So to me it follows that if the chemistry of the ocean is changing now, the types of life that it can support will change, too.

Whether life collapses catastrophically, as it has only five other times in the history of life on the planet, depends on how quickly and how deeply the ocean changes. For example, during the Great Dying of the Permian extinction 250 million years ago, when the sea lost its oxygen, about 95 per cent of life in the ocean vanished from the global gene bank. Including a lot of plankton.

However, in the whole history of human thought, the idea that life could change so dramatically is new. Young, writing long before the current ecological crisis was understood, noted that it was only in the nineteenth century that scientists realised that the geography and climate of the world had not always been the same.

He added: '. . . but only in the last twenty years has the full extent of the change become appreciated . . . To understand why animals and plants have changed, and how they have become spread over the earth, we need knowledge of the distribution and composition of the land, sea and atmosphere at various times in the past, as well as information about the temperature and other physical conditions.'

In short, chemistry and physics determine biology. And future chemistry and physics will determine future biology.

The revelation now, sixty years on, is that it is our hand on the switch.

It brings me back to coccoliths, and to the scientists' trick of deconstructing the question. In scientific circles, this is known as performing 'the big so what'.

So the coccoliths, here on the planet for at least 150 million years, won't like an acidic sea, may not produce their limestone shells and store carbon in the deep ocean. *So what.* Does any of that really matter? Won't another type of plankton—or many other types—take over the coccoliths' planetary functions in good time if they vanish? Is this scientific race to find out about plankton really necessary? Couldn't humans just noodle along, having faith that the planetary systems will somehow right themselves?

Standing here on the fabled Plymouth Hoe overlooking the Sound, this strikes me as a profoundly moral question. Can humans, knowing that human civilisation itself is at stake and that the outcome is uncertain, choose to turn a blind eye?

I turn to Young for answers. He writes—quite coolly—about what sets humans apart from other animals.

He compares the human brain to that of apes. The brains are arranged in a similar way, except that the occipital and frontal lobes in humans are better developed. The occipital lobes give us the gifts of sight and visualisation. That is, the ability to see in a physical sense. Even more important to our survival, Young argues, are the highly developed frontal lobes.

He writes: 'The frontal lobes, so far as is known, serve to maintain the balance between caution or restraint and sustained active pursuit of distant ends, which, above all else, ensures human survival in such a variety of situations, and makes possible the social life and use of language by which so great a population is maintained.'

Connected to these front lobes, of course, is the quintessential human power of abstract thought—the ability to see metaphorically. To understand. It is, Young asserts, what makes us human.

So when I go back to the question of whether we should just sit back and let the universe unfold, I have to conclude that it is not fully human to do that. 'Fully human' is to exercise restraint while we pursue far-off goals; to imagine that the future has the capacity to be worse than today; to recognise the signs that things are changing, and not in a straight line.

We are creating a new future on an unprecedented scale. That part is incontrovertible. The unknown is what future we will choose to create.

In all of humanity's 150,000-year history, it seems to me that this is the moment to harness the human gift of being able to plan.

The National Marine Aquarium in Plymouth was one of the first public aquaria in the world and the first in Britain. The original building, opened in 1888, comprised tanks in picture frames, seen from dark corridors. This new building, with its soaring ceilings, broad vistas and inventive displays set right on the shore, opened in 1998.

Kelvin Boot, the aquarium's director, has a wit both quick and sharp. His sense of humour is dry. He is one of the few non-scientists I will interview at Plymouth and we bond immediately. By a pleasing irony, the aquarium is next to Plymouth's bustling fish market. 'It's a wonderful juxtaposition,' Boot says, laughing and pointing to the market. 'You can buy them by the kilo over there. Here we spend money to keep them alive.'

The fish market next door actually provides some valuable research. Aquarium scientists nip over every now and again to see what's for sale. It helps them track changes in what's being caught in local waters.

As Boot explains, the changes are legion. When this building opened in 1998, the centrepiece was the Mediterranean tank. It's the deepest tank in Britain, a soaring mass of water teeming with creatures. You can stand under a thick, concave sheet of acrylic that reaches from the floor to far above your head and watch fish from another part of the world swim above you.

Except that these fish are now not exactly from another part of the world. Today, these fish also live wild in British waters. The ocean off the coast of Devon has warmed up enough in just a decade that fish once caught in Provence are now common this far north.

A few years ago, Boot tells me, some of the scientists found some unusual very young fish. So the aquarium raised them, only to discover that they were Couch's sea bream, a species that had not reproduced in English waters in living memory.

The classic Mediterranean trigger fish is breeding in British estuaries now, almost to the point of becoming a nuisance. Mediterranean sharks have been spotted here and there, and barracuda, more commonly residents of tropical and subtropical waters, now live in the ocean off Devon.

If the fish are moving, does it follow that plankton, the ocean's vagabonds, are too?

To find the answer, I turn to the Marine Biological Association, the draughty home to so many Nobel Prize winners and to the Sir Alister Hardy Foundation for Ocean Science, known as SAHFOS. It is a world of wonder. While science in the world outside this building is moving proudly at breakneck speed, at SAHFOS the technology for tracking plankton has remained unchanged for decades. Here are rooms containing several handmade gunmetal bronze and brass contraptions, next to what looks like a watchmaker's repair shop where Barnard mends the broken. There are no electronics. In fact, there's little in this place that you couldn't have found in the Camden Town of Charles Dickens.

These are some of SAHFOS's fleet of continuous plankton recorders. For a flat £50 honorarium they hitch rides with friendly ships whose crews tow them through the waters of the world so the machines can take samples of what plankton are where during what time.

The prototype was a simple disk dragged by a wire behind a boat. When the disk came out of the water, the crew would eyeball it to see if it had caught any green gunk, meaning plankton. If there were plankton, that meant there would be fish too.

The idea then was not to find out much about plankton themselves but just to use their presence or absence to increase the fish catch.

The devices are more sophisticated now, but just barely. These days they are rectangular boxes with tail fins that contain infinitesimally finely spun silk cloth to catch the larger plankton. Each piece of silk is just one four-thousandth of an inch thick, rolled around a compartment packed with cotton batting that soaks up formalin from another compartment deep within the box.

At one time, trying to be modern, some staff tried using nylon cloth instead of the fine silk. It was a disaster: hard to fold and not thin enough to do the job. Now SAHFOS supplies lengths of this fine, plankton-catching silk cloth to sister surveys in the United States and Tasmania.

If the machines haven't changed in more than seventy years, though, the goals of using them have changed profoundly. Now the idea is to examine the plankton themselves, to try to answer the globally critical and elusive question. Whither plankton?

Across the hall is another dark and cramped room where scientists are examining rolls of fine silk that have come back from the sea. They have a roster of about 200 phytoplankton, or tiny marine plants, that they look for, as well as about 300 types of zooplankton, or marine animals.

These scientists are using bespoke microscopes worth thousands of pounds, some dating back fifty years. Even a single-lensed microscope, called a monocular microscope, is still in use.

One of the scientists shows me what she's looking at under her scope. It is a little crustacean, a zooplankton called *Calanus helgolandicus* from the South Irish Sea. This fellow is not a *Calanus finmarchicus*, the type of plankton once rampant through these waters. She describes the differences between the two, trying to guide me as I peer through the microscope.

C. finmarchicus has a fifth swimming leg and is more regularly shaped, smaller and rounded. *C. helgolandicus* is larger, has only four swimming legs and is concave.

I'm stumped. I can barely make out legs or curves or anything. The scientist chuckles a bit. This particular plankton is folded over onto itself, so it's a bit hard to see, she acknowledges. But, she says, you get used to telling one from the other.

Why does any of this matter?

The *C. helgolandicus* is an important source of food for larval fish. It's moved northward by an extraordinary 1000 kilometres in the past forty years, replacing some of the *C. finmarchicus* that used to live here. But this new type of plankton is present in far smaller numbers than its predecessor—there's been a drop of about 70 per cent in sheer biomass, or the weight of its living matter.

I go upstairs to the office of SAHFOS director Peter Burkill to see what he and his colleague Martin Edwards can tell me about the implications of these peculiar changes to the plankton population. We have to talk above the call of the gulls on the Sound and the wind whistling in the windows.

Edwards, the assistant director in charge of research, is one of the world's experts on the cycles in the ocean that determine such things as why one phytoplankton blooms just in time to feed the animals that need it. It's a field known as phenology.

As the climate changes and the ocean warms up, these finely tuned biological cycles are getting out of sync. It's called mismatch, and it's what happened to Joanie Kleypas's monkeys in Costa Rica that died when the fruit didn't come.

One of Edwards's key findings, using research from the plankton recorders downstairs, has been that the mismatch in the North Sea is already advanced and runs far beyond the tiny crustaceans his colleagues are looking at today.

In a paper in the 19 August 2004 issue of *Nature*, Edwards

and a colleague write that the marine timing dynamics 'may have already been radically altered . . . and will continue to do so in the coming decades if the climate continues to warm at its present rate'. For example, the little, ferociously abundant diatoms, which are marine algae with shells of silica, bloom in the spring just like plants on land. Traditionally, this has marked the beginning of a spring feeding and breeding frenzy in the ocean.

The problem is that the trigger for diatoms to bloom comes from the length of the day, rather than the temperature of the water. So their bloom time has stayed the same over the decades as the surface of the ocean has warmed.

Other creatures, though, are triggered to bloom or release eggs by the temperature of the water. As the temperature has increased, that timing has moved forwards. Edwards found, for instance, that the peak abundance for the larvae of such creatures as sea urchins and brittle stars moved forward a staggering forty-seven days between 1958 and 2002.

He's fascinated with what these changes will mean for the fishery, especially when combined with chronic overfishing. But he's also looking at whether there are wider, so far unknown, implications for the plankton-driven cycles of oxygen, carbon, nitrogen and silica.

There will be consequences, he tells me, and they will probably be negative.

Burkill, who has been tossing in comments from time to time, springs to life at the mention of the big picture. This is where his heart is, in how the changes to ocean and climate will affect the whole planetary system.

He has made a career of studying even smaller plankton than the bronze recorders downstairs can capture, including the bacterial sort that help distribute the critical minerals in the ocean's depths to the larger plankton that need them to grow.

He starts to tell me a story about these tiniest plankton—one of those causal chains of events in this complex system of ocean and air that I could never have imagined.

During the 1990s, he and a group of other scientists spent a great deal of time doing shipboard research at a hotspot in the Arabian Sea, at the top of the Indian Ocean.

As concentrations of carbon dioxide and other greenhouse gases increase in the atmosphere and change the global climate, the powerful southwest monsoon blowing over the Arabian Sea becomes even stronger. Its winds churn up the water more and bring extra chemical nutrients from the deep water closer to the top. Just like the crop fertilisers that run into the Gulf of Mexico, these nutrients push the phytoplankton into an orgy of growing and reproducing.

These marine plants die quickly and fall to the bottom of the Arabian Sea. There are so many plant bodies that the ocean's bacteria, in turn, have their own feeding frenzy, producing vast quantities of methane, nitrous oxide and sometimes, as oxygen is depleted, hydrogen sulfide as waste products.

Already the Arabian Sea has far more than the usual oceanic concentration of methane and some of that is flowing into the atmosphere. One of Burkill's papers calculated that the flow of methane from the Arabian Sea into the atmosphere is five times greater than the ocean's average, still a tiny amount in the scheme of things. Methane is a far more potent greenhouse gas than carbon dioxide, although it lasts for a shorter time in the atmosphere. Most of this plankton-generated methane is caught under the surface of the Arabian Sea because the surface and the deeps are separated into layers that are hard to mix. But over the past thirty years, the distance between the layers in parts of the Arabian Sea has become alarmingly narrower.

If the store of deep-sea methane should ever breach the surface—think of a nasty belch—it would release a tremendous amount of methane into the atmosphere. In turn, that could prove such an assault on the climate that it would represent a tipping point, the moment when the global system begins to work hard not to recover its old state but to create a new one.

As he's been talking, Burkill has been moving around this light-filled office, collecting bunches of scientific papers to give to me. He'd like to go back to the Arabian Sea to do more research there, he tells me as I leave. He wants to know what the plankton there are doing right now.

I'm staggering by the time I get back out onto the Hoe. It feels as though the more I learn about plankton, the more questions I have. And as for the biggest question of all—whether any of these changes will affect the global ocean's ability to support life— that's also the least settled of all.

Humanity has tackled other complex issues, like discrimination based on skin colour, gender or sexual orientation. For society to be convinced that these were happening and needed to be made right, a whole bunch of dots needed to show up on a screen.

On the issue of discrimination based on skin colour in the 1950s and 1960s in America, for example, a classic technique was to look at the vital signs of the black community as a whole. These were considered proxies.

What was the black infant mortality rate compared to the white? What was the black life expectancy compared to the white? What proportion of African-Americans owned property compared to whites? What was the average black income compared to the white? Were any African-Americans in positions of corporate or political power?

Each of these individual indicators had exceptions. But when you connected the dots, they told you a story.

The story of plankton has a similar trajectory. It's hellishly complicated. But when you take out the background shadows, it's clear that plankton are extraordinarily important to the workings of the planet, that they are changing dramatically in a very short time and that the potential implications of this are severe.

It's also clear that some of the best minds in the world are working feverishly to figure out the implications. Plankton are telling us a story that we ignore at our peril.

By the time I get back to the Laboratory building and the office of Manuel Barange, director of the Global Ocean Ecosystem Dynamics program (GLOBEC), all I really want is reassurance. Luckily Barange, trained as a fisheries scientist, is a philosopher at heart.

GLOBEC is a muscular international group devoted to answering precisely the sort of questions I've been asking, Barange explains. When it was set up about two decades ago, its goal was to find out what was happening below the fish. Even by 1999, when GLOBEC became part of the blue-chip International Geosphere-Biosphere Programme, the understanding of global change was 'still ropey', Barange explains, meaning that it wasn't the accepted wisdom.

Today the GLOBEC program is all big picture, all the time.

It's incredibly hard, he says. 'This problem is more complex than we ever imagined. Every time you solve a little bit of the puzzle, you see that there's another huge part of the puzzle unsolved over there.'

For example, Barange's team is trying to develop a vulnerability index that will predict changes to the productivity or metabolism of parts of the ocean.

Key to the whole thing, says Barange, is the need to deal with the climate issues in conjunction with human issues. In other words, humans are now an intrinsic part of the marine system.

'It's not one without the other,' he says. 'It's never humans and not climate. It's always both. This is frontier we have to break. We need to break disciplines.'

We talk for another hour or so and I'm starting to see glim mers of hope.

Near the end, he leaves me with this: 'The scale of the solution has to be to the scale of the problem.'

It is the scariest thing I have heard yet.

CHAPTER 5

READING THE VITAL SIGNS: FECUNDITY

Panama: The blind wisdom of the coral

Being a successful coral means having a superb sense of timing. And not the arbitrary, human-built timing that measures from past to future, but the primeval sort that counts off rhythms. In other words, not progress but pattern. Not the measurement of something fleeting but of a constant.

Spawning corals survive because they understand mysterious signals that come once a year from an alignment of the sun, the earth and the moon. All year these primitive animals, who have neither brains nor eyes nor the ability to move, laboriously store energy to prepare eggs and sperm for the moment of the spawn. And on that one night a year, between five and seven days after the biggest full moon of summer, at a moment so preordained that it can be measured down to the human minute, billions of them ritualistically send forth all this genetic material into the wide ocean in an ancient pageant designed to make baby corals. It's a once-a-year orgy of group sex.

Humans only figured out in the mid-1980s—during night dives on Australia's Great Barrier Reef—that corals reproduce this way. But ancestors of modern corals have been found in fossil records going back 450 million years and it's a safe bet that some version of this annual rite has been going on for about that length of time.

Corals sense movements in the universe that humans appear to have forgotten. Viewed through the lens of non-human time, they seem to be the ultimate survivors.

More than survivors, though, they are progenitors. The bony reefs the corals build are the nurseries of the ocean, home to at least a quarter of all known life forms in the sea. Because the planet has far more ocean than land, and because the ocean holds so much life, coral reefs are biologically among the most critical parts of the planet. Yet the coral reefs are also where all the important human-caused threats to the seas intersect. The biggest of these is global climate change, which is affecting ocean temperature, volume, acidity and possibly salinity, and maybe even the structure of the currents in ways scientists are just starting to calculate. Moreover, overfishing and pollution are harming the ecology of the reefs.

The result is that 20 per cent of the world's reefs have already been destroyed and another 50 per cent are in trouble. In the Caribbean, 80 per cent have died in the past three decades. So here in the Caribbean, if the corals are still reproducing, in perishingly hot waters, that will be a sign that the ocean still has some moxie, that it has not fallen into reproductive unconsciousness.

These primitive marine animals have more to teach us. What would we see if we could view the planet not through the linear time of human stories but through the multidimensional time of corals and their ilk? Would we see more clearly, recognise the great dangers we are running? Could we, too, become survivors in the long game of evolution?

I have decided that I need to watch the corals as they spawn in response to the lunar cycle, to look for life in the larger theme of death. And this is how I have ended up arriving in Panama on the night of the biggest full moon of the summer, on day zero in the lead-up to the spawning of the corals.

Nancy Knowlton is the corals' timekeeper. A superstar marine biologist who is now the first holder of the Sant chair in marine science at the Smithsonian's National Museum of Natural History in Washington, DC, she has also worked extensively with the Smithsonian Tropical Research Institute in Panama City and with the Scripps Institution of Oceanography in La Jolla, California. Tall and rangy, with a thick fringe of brown hair covering her forehead, Knowlton is best known for showing scientists that the oceans hold far more species than anyone had thought, probably by a factor of ten. She's also renowned for being able to identify marine animals that are difficult to tell apart by conventional methods, the so-called cryptic species of the seas.

For instance, she was the first to realise that the corals we're here to monitor—*Montastraea franksi*, *M. annularis* and *M. faveolata*—are three species instead of one. These three are the slow-growing workhorses of the Caribbean reefs, with boulder-shaped bony structures that can get as big as a house. Understanding the future of the savaged Caribbean reefs means knowing these *Montastraea* inside and out.

For some reason she can't fully explain, Knowlton loves corals. Perhaps it's the challenge of trying to understand an animal that early generations of scientists thought was a plant. Perhaps it's the pleasing tension between how primitive they are and how ecologically critical. Or the sheer intellectual puzzle of trying to figure them out when most scientists don't bother.

The love affair started in 1980 when Hurricane Allen, one of the strongest hurricanes in recorded history, hit the Jamaican reefs Knowlton was studying. Four days later, before the storm had fully subsided, Knowlton was underwater at the Dancing Lady reef in Jamaica's Discovery Bay to catalogue the damage.

The reef was pulverised. Knowlton figured she would study it for years to come to chronicle its recovery. But it never came back. It just kept dying, hit by disease and hindered by an ecosystem that had already been badly damaged by overfishing. It was the beginning of the end of the Jamaican reefs, the textbook case of a biological worst-case scenario.

Once Knowlton worked out that the lack of fish and the health of the corals were connected, she had to keep going, keep studying the corals. She's become one of just a small group of people in the world who understand them.

For one thing, the hard bony bits that we terrestrial creatures think of as corals—the pieces we put on our mantles and wear as jewellery—are the inanimate parts of the animals, the calcified base the corals continually add to. The way Knowlton puts it, it's as if we grew bones out of the bottom of our feet and kept getting taller. Or like a tree trunk that grows taller throughout its life so its leaves can reach for the sun. Except these bony pieces are stone, created by the coral from the carbon and calcium in the ocean through a simple chemical process.

The shape of these bony pieces distinguishes some corals from others, but that's not precise enough to tell species apart. It's also key to look at the living animal: the flaccid layer perhaps 100 cells deep that covers just the upper surface of the bony structure.

This has been one of the great problems of identifying corals and many other marine animals. Generations of taxonomists have looked at them on land, dead. But they look far different alive than they do dried or frozen.

Knowlton decided early on that if she wanted to study marine animals, she needed to go where they were, become part of their environment, no matter how foreign it felt to her. It means she has spent a great deal of her life underwater, attached to a scuba tank. Now, it's second nature to her. She sees creatures that most humans cannot imagine exist.

She loves Panama, too, despite the fact that she and her daughter (now grown) were taken hostage from a Smithsonian research station by several Panamanians when the United States army invaded this country on 20 December 1989. Forced to walk barefoot across hills for most of a day and kept without food for two, Knowlton and her daughter, along with nearly a dozen Smithsonian employees, were finally abandoned by their captors. A US Army helicopter pilot found them.

Knowlton doesn't dwell on that. At one point in our journey together she says she'll tell me the whole story, but we never quite get to it. The closest we come is when she shows me a photograph of the whole group of hostages taken after they'd been whisked back to the American army base. It's pinned up beside her desk at the Smithsonian's research base, along with drawings from her daughter's early school years. In the picture Knowlton's smile is huge, relieved. Her daughter stands close.

Knowlton talks of the grace and friendliness of the Panamanian people, the ferocious beauty of the rain storms that she watches with glee from the balcony of her flat in Panama City, the engineering feat that led to the building of the Panama Canal. Now she is based in the United States, and her flat in Panama City has become a refuge for graduate students in marine biology and for itinerant academics. And authors.

Knowlton and I arrive at her flat to stay for a couple of nights before leaving for the Smithsonian's research station at Bocas del Toro on the Caribbean side of Panama, where, we hope, the corals will be spawning in about six days.

Like high tide, the dawn and sunset, a full moon has a specific time. That time changes month after month, coinciding with the precise moment when the sun and moon are on opposite sides of the earth.

This month it happened on 18 September at 2:01 a.m. Universal Time, or Greenwich Mean Time. According to Knowlton's painstaking years of study and calculations, this means that the corals will spawn about six days from now. The *M. franksi* will let their slick of genetic material go 100 minutes after sunset; *M. annularis* and *M. faveolata* will do it another 100 minutes after that.

It's not clear why this happens after the biggest full moon of the summer. Again, it's one of those cues that the corals recognise and humans don't. One theory is that the corals respond to an absence of moonlight. The time between sunset and moonrise is longest on the night about six days after the biggest full moon of summer. How they know this moonless stretch is coming is another mystery.

It is shortly after dawn on day two and Knowlton is anxious. I can tell because her foot is in constant movement—up and down, up and down. We are on a Jetstream 31 flying from Panama City to the rickety resort town of Bocas del Toro in the north of Panama. The Smithsonian has had a marine research station here for several years, on a prime piece of the Caribbean. Originally a sweltering shack, the station has become more sophisticated in recent years. Not only are there modern, air-conditioned labs filled with pristine equipment, but also a decorative man-made pond filled with caymans that winds around the buildings, and landscaped grounds complete with hanging poisonous snakes that the gardener periodically chases away.

The facility itself is all ready. About a dozen students and scientists from all over the US, and two from Taiwan, have assembled at the research station at the behest of the corals, with hundreds of kilograms of diving gear and lab materials, to help Knowlton figure out whether these enigmatic animals are successfully reproducing.

The plan is to scuba dive onto the reef for hours at a time, chronicle exactly when the corals pop their tiny pink bundles of sperm and eggs, follow the bundles to the surface of the sea, collect some of the spawn and then stay up most of the night checking the eggs under a three-dimensional microscope to see how many get fertilised. It's an expensive and time-consuming enterprise. So her team is primed and in place. This is not what she's worried about.

Her concern is the corals. Although she and her team have correctly predicted the timing of the mass spawn for years, there's always the chance that the corals won't do what everyone is expecting. Knowlton might have mistimed the event, for example, which would be an expensive mistake, given the cost of bringing in all this high-powered expertise. There's an off-chance that the corals decided to spawn last month, for example. Or that this year they will decide to go for broke a few days early.

It could also be that Knowlton's timekeeping is correct but the corals are too sick and listless to spawn. Now she has slipped off her shoe in the airplane. Her bare foot is moving nonstop. She is wondering what the corals are doing. Are they making their bundles of sperm and eggs? Are they responding to the hidden cues from the moon, earth and sun? And what if the corals don't spawn? What will that say about the future?

As soon as we arrive at the research station at Bocas del Toro, we get bad news. Davey Kline, a coral reef ecologist who was one of Knowlton's students and who lives in Panama, has been diving in the reefs all around this section of the Caribbean. The corals are badly bleached. In fact, it's as bad an episode as he's ever seen.

Bleaching is one of the great modern scourges of the coral. It means that the symbiotic relationship between the coral animal and the algae that live in its cells is breaking down. The algae, which photosynthesise the sun's rays to feed the corals and also give the corals their jewel-like colours, die, leaving behind white coral tissue. The corals starve unless they can attract more algae.

I ask what causes the bleaching.

Knowlton doesn't hesitate: the water is too warm for the algae to live.

Why is the water warm?

Again, the answer comes right away: it's global climate change, the heating up of the atmosphere—and, therefore, the global ocean—through high concentrations of greenhouse gases.

And, as Knowlton points out, both the frequency and the intensity of coral bleaching have been increasing steadily since the 1980s, in lockstep with ever higher concentrations of these gases.

There is one bright spot, though: Kline notes that Knowlton's three species of *Montastraea* don't seem to be as badly bleached as some of the 100 or so other species of corals in the Caribbean.

Knowlton breaks out into huge smile. The team laughs in relief.

'They've put up with our lights and our chisels for so long, the temperature doesn't bother them,' she says. She knows, of course, that it's something different. Maybe that the specific type of algae that live in the *Montastraea* can take higher temperatures than the algae in other corals. Maybe it's something no one has thought of yet. Another coral mystery to work on.

By 10:45 a.m. the air-conditioned lab where Knowlton's coral experiments will take place has been fully kitted out. I begin to think of it as the war room, the strategic centre of this minutely planned operation.

Students and scientists have set up cupboard after cupboard of carefully labelled silicon tubes, Petri dishes, pipettes, vials, culture trays, centrifuge tubes, hammers, chisels, buoys and lines, torches, batteries, knives, wire brushes, hundreds of metres of bright orange flagging tape, and dozens upon dozens of glow sticks. High-powered laptops are plugged in on several of the counters, blasting music and spitting out data.

Knowlton is standing in front of a large whiteboard, marker in hand, making meticulous lists.

It's only when we embark on our reconnaissance mission in the afternoon to find the transect of corals that Knowlton has been tracking for four years that the extent of the bleaching becomes clear. Knowlton points over the side of the boat to show me. Then I see what she sees: an expanse of neon white under the boat. Even through several metres of water, it looks alien.

One of the students, Nikki Fogarty—who is trying to make a career of studying corals—shakes her head. It's depressing, she says. She's not sure whether there will be enough corals to study by the time she's finished graduate work.

She's been scuba diving for the past fifteen years, since she was just a kid, and has seen the mounting destruction close up. Now every coral reef symposium she attends shows charts of continual global declines in the number of healthy reefs. At those symposia, as on this big boat, there's a question no one wants to deal with: is all of this research too little, too late?

Soon, though, the joy of being caught up in studying the corals takes over. Knowlton and nearly a dozen others will be underwater for hours on end, right down to the final measures of compressed air. At the end, some of them will start snorkelling because all the scuba tanks on board are empty.

Because this bit of the reef has been studied for so long, many of the coral colonies have been marked with tags. But since the last spawning a year ago, the tags have become encrusted with ocean life, taken back by the sea.

Today the crew has to laboriously find each tag, scrape it so the number is visible and make a notation of where it is. This is critical to the record keeping of the whole enterprise. And it's exhausting. But it's the only way the team can keep track of whether an individual coral spawns and compare it to what happened in other years.

I'm still on the boat. It's a huge, sweltering creature, affectionately dubbed 'the floating classroom', with room for eight plus their diving gear and extra tanks. I realise after everyone else has jumped in that I can't make myself go under the surface of the sea. It must be primal, this fear, residue of a species whose distant ancestors abandoned water in favour of land. Some people can overcome it, can flourish in the ocean. I can think only of death.

The deeps seem unknowable. Throughout human history we have seen the surface of the sea while imagining and fearing what's below. Down the ages, through legend and myth, we have made the oceans the home of monsters, shape-shifters, demons and danger. Here are the gaping teeth that make us shudder, the whirlpools that suck us to places beyond redemption, the predators we can neither hear nor smell.

It's the flat two dimensions of the surface we've tried to master: the trade routes; the best fishing spots; the arts of avoiding storms, shoals and icebergs. For very good swimmers, the known sea extended perhaps 30 metres down, as long as the breath could hold.

My urge is to go so much deeper—both physically and psychologically—to know what it's like to be part of the sea in all of its dimensions. And then to understand them across the long fourth dimension of time—from past to present to future. If you put all four dimensions together you get an integrated whole, a coral-style understanding of life in which things happen in patterns, in cycles, in ancient rhythms not easily visible. Putting the four dimensions together is what the Australian Aborigines think of as the Dreamtime, or anywhen.

In the span of human history, only a few of our species have had the ability to consider even the third dimension of the ocean— its vast depth—much less the three dimensions over time. It was only in the 1920s and 1930s that humans figured out how to compress air and send people as far down as 150 metres. And it was the 1970s before deep-diving submersibles routinely got as far down as about 1500 metres. And that's still a small fraction of the real depth of the ocean—which is on average 3794 metres deep and at its deepest 11,034 metres.

Of course, it's not just about depth. It's also about volume, the three dimensions together.

Life on land and in the air occupies a thin layer above the surface. Most of land life is right on the surface, with the exception of a few high-flying birds and the odd skyscraper. It's a narrow third dimension, in other words.

In the ocean, this dimension is thick. Life runs across in all directions and down to the bottom. The dimensions move and connect on a scale that land dwellers can barely fathom. In fact, when you add up the earth's biosphere, or the part of it that is available for living creatures, the land portion comes out to just 1 per cent of that total volume.

Not only that, but if you look at the phylum level of the tree of life, the second highest level of taxonomic organisation, underneath kingdom, it's astonishingly sea based, too. Of the thirty-three phyla of animals on earth, twenty-eight are in the ocean and only eleven are on land. (There's overlap.) Of those, thirteen are restricted to the ocean and evolved there. Just one, the ancient, slug-like *Onychophora*, evolved on land and is restricted to it. Not only that, but animals in the ocean—not hampered by the land's gravity—boast twice as many body blueprints as animals on land. It's a far more diverse and rich living space than the land.

Tuesday, day three in the build-up from full moon to spawn, is the day of victories. Knowlton and eight other members of her crew are in the boat by 12:15 p.m., chisels and magnifying glasses in hand. The water is clear, the day sunny. We can see easily to the bottom of the transect; corals loom under the boat. Today, I am determined to see them close up.

The others plunge in, attached to tanks. I resolutely press my mask and snorkel to my face, put on borrowed flippers, roll over the side.

My nose fills with water—the mask doesn't fit. But I can see corals and the whole marked section of the reef where the scientific studies will take place. I'm hanging close to the boat, just above Allen Chen, a marine biologist from Taiwan who is here to see the action, and one of his graduate students. They are moving slowly, deliberately. This is not a business for show-offs.

The water is full of moon jellyfish today. They sting, but not like some of the more dangerous jellies, such as the man-o'-war. Knowlton has already given me the spiel on those fellows. Before she went under, I asked her—attempting to be matter-of-fact— what can kill me out here. She pondered this a minute.

'You know about the man-o'-wars?' she asked.

'Well, actually, no.'

'They have tentacles hanging down. If you got them wrapped around your face, near your nervous system, that would be a problem. Try to avoid them,' she advised.

Hanging on the surface, moving with the waves, checking for bundles of tentacles, I watch the moon jellies warming themselves in the rays of the afternoon sun. The sun comes down in shafts, refracted through the waves.

I see brain coral. So named because it looks like a human brain. And loads of *M. franksi*, Knowlton's beloved species.

They're frankly hard to bond with. Unmoving. Seemingly dead. These are not the warm and fuzzy mammals that most conservation organisations put to the fore to convince humans that life is valuable. I'm thinking about those cute pandas and those adorable baby seals. Even lemurs. These corals could be so many rocks strewn on the shallow ocean floor.

A while later, Knowlton bounces up. She's been down on the reef with her chisel, whacking off tiny bits of coral to see whether they're 'ripe', meaning, whether they're making eggs and sperm for the spawning. She's grinning, tension dissolved. The timing is correct. The spawn is going to happen.

Knowlton has also brought up buckets of sea creatures from the reef for me to look at under the three-dimensional microscope. Once we get back to land, we take some of these marine goodies up to a lab.

She puts a tiny piece of reef, covered by sea water, under the microscope. It's solid with organisms. At least twenty-five, at a conservative count. Here are the bizarre bryozoans, who make stacks of clear glassy boxes. Almost turrets. Their feeding apparatus emerges from a hole at the top of the stacks. There's a barnacle, its feathery appendages coming out the top. Here's a clam, too small to see with the naked eye.

There is a brittle star, the smaller and more flexible cousin of a starfish. Over here, several types of sponge, some bright orange and others chartreuse.

There is a sea anemone, which Knowlton thinks of as a coral without a skeleton. It's hungry and has captured a minuscule shrimp. Here, a worm.

This minute piece of reef is swarming with life.

Knowlton is in her element, finding these creatures, handling them with utmost gentleness. She must have spent hundreds of hours looking at similar pieces of life under a microscope, yet she's as absorbed in this batch as if it were her first.

The question hangs over us: if there's this much diversity of life in a tiny piece of one type of reef, how much is there in a whole reef ecosystem? Putting a number on what's there and what's being lost will be Knowlton's defining work, the thing no one has done before.

Day four. Great sorrow. Fogarty and a helper, Katie Lotterhos, went out last night to capture some eggs and sperm from a type of coral that is supposed to spawn a day or two before the *Montastraea*. They are looking at the elkhorn corals, *Acropora palmata* and *A. cervicornis*, which are heavily endangered in the Caribbean and elsewhere. In the last several years 80 to 90 per cent of the elkhorns in the Caribbean have died.

Fogarty and Lotterhos were trying to get enough elkhorn sperm and eggs to produce offspring between the two species in the lab and then grow them to find out whether these hybrids would thrive. They spent a full day taping off a countertop in the lab into a matrix and labelling each square, painstakingly measuring distilled sea water in pipettes. They went out in high spirits last night to capture the spawn.

Then . . . nothing. No spawn. No evidence of spawn. The human calculators of time have been skunked.

Knowlton holds back from comment. She knows it's devilishly difficult to predict when corals will spit out their bundles of eggs and sperm, and she's not ready to criticise graduate students who have mistimed things. Still, she knows that her *Montastraea* are likely to spawn on day six, two days from now, and that means we go through a full-scale operation tonight, as if today were the day. She's not about to miss anything if she can help it.

That means I have to do my first night snorkel tonight. She gives me my day's assignment: by dusk, she wants me to be able to dive to 3 metres with a snorkel. It's a very different skill from swimming placidly along the surface, as I have been doing in seas all over the world. She assigns one of her graduate students, Kristen Marhaver, a brilliant geneticist, to teach me.

Marhaver, whose name means 'keeper of the harbour' in German, reminds me of a mermaid. Long, slender, with a shock of red hair, she seems more at ease in the water than out of it.

We take the boat and get our gear on at a shallow reef neither of us has seen before. Marhaver does an elegant five-minute lesson on diving with a 'snork' while I try to keep up. Then she starts with direct incentives. She dives to the bottom to look at what's there, challenging me to follow.

She loves every creature. Every molecule. She can't keep her hands off them. She keeps surfacing, enchanted, with new things to show me. Her knowledge of reefs is encyclopaedic.

One quick look around and she sees that there are far too many algae. In the good reef/bad reef rubric of Katharina Fabricius of the Australian Institute of Marine Science in Townsville, this would be a bad reef. Marhaver explains that if this reef were healthy it would have loads of sea urchins that would eat these algae. In fact, there used to be so many sea urchins in the Caribbean that scientists considered them a nuisance. Then disease wiped out the urchins.

With the sea urchins gone, the algae take over. Two specific types have flourished, Marhaver tells me. One is bitter. Even fish fed pellets will spit out the pellets if this type of algae is slipped into them. The second type of algae is filled with calcium carbonate—the same stuff the corals make their bony bits out of. It's too crunchy for any sea creatures but the urchins to eat. So the algae keep growing.

It's terrible for corals. Baby corals need hard surfaces to settle on; these algae keep everything slick.

The fish are absent, fished out by locals. We see one crab. No lobsters. No sharks. No baby corals, just the older, established ones, smothered with algae. It's a wasteland.

Marhaver puts on her scuba tank and leaves me to play. Periodically she surfaces to point out something to me. I try and try to descend, hold my breath, kick as hard as I can. Finally I decide I need some weights around my waist. I am, as Knowlton delicately puts it, rather buoyant. Meaning I have a nice solid layer of fat that keeps me on the surface, like an inflated inner tube.

It's a bit crushing. But not as bad as when I try to hoist myself into the boat. I've forgotten to let down the ladder beside the engine; it's caught tight with stretchy cords. Everyone else is underwater, probably for another hour or two. I keep thinking about man-o'-wars. About whether there's a shark in the Caribbean that hasn't been killed off and might like a buoyant morsel of human for lunch.

Hanging in the water near the boat, I consider Mark Denny's *Air and Water: The Biology and Physics of Life's Media*. It describes the physical differences of air and ocean. These different media—sea water compared to air—help determine how different creatures are shaped, how they hear and see.

So, for example, air is twenty billion times less conductive than water. One of the fascinating, relatively unexplored aspects of life in the ocean is how marine creatures communicate through electric currents and how they might pick up electrical signals from deep within the earth's core. Denny calls this the 'sixth sense'.

Every time a muscle contracts—say, when an animal breathes or tries to heave herself over the side of a classroom boat without a ladder—the body sends off electrical signals that can be read by other animals.

This could be a clue to the blind wisdom of the corals. They certainly respond to light, to pressure, to chemical signals from other creatures. Could they respond somehow to electricity in the water?

I'm lost in these thoughts until I remember that Denny says sharks and rays are among the most alert to electrical impulses. I decide to remain very still.

Marhaver shows up unexpectedly. She's come back to check on me. I explain that I can't get back in the boat without a ladder. She looks at me quizzically and slips effortlessly over the boat's side to let down the ladder before popping back down into the sea.

By 6:53 p.m. it's pitch black and we're back out at the transect, in the midst of what I can only think of as a military operation, to witness the corals in the act of the spawn. No one believes that today is the day, but we're acting as though it is for practice purposes.

Don Levitan, a wiry marine biologist from Florida State University and Knowlton's research partner on the coral spawning, has arrived with three more students. It's now a team of more than a dozen highly educated scientists looking for coral spawn in the waters of the Caribbean.

Underwater, the mapped section is lit up with chemical glow sticks to show the divers where the whole expanse is. Each pair of divers is assigned to one point on the transect with the task of examining each of hundreds of coral polyps at that point for a total of nearly three hours, with one 10-minute space in the middle to change compressed air tanks. I'll be snorkelling on top of the water.

We're all waiting for the corals. The divers are munching on chocolate bars for a last-minute burst of quick energy.

Knowlton sees the worms first. Perfect circles of bright white light on the surface of the sea around our boat. They are female glow worms, trying to attract males. In a few minutes we see luminescent puffs beneath them. These are the males, drawn by the light, spraying the females with semen. Knowlton grins. The glow worms always mate one or two days before the corals spawn.

By 8 p.m. the divers are in, eyes glued to the corals, watching for signs of the bundles of eggs and sperm. Each individual coral of these three *Montastraea* species is a hermaphrodite and produces both sperm and eggs, bound together chemically. A few minutes before the corals release these bundles, the bundles 'set'. That means the bundles rise through the flesh of the corals and sit at the single orifice, ready to burst at a signal that only they can discern. Then, buoyed by the fat in the eggs, the bundles rise to the surface in a slick, and break up into just sperm and just eggs.

It's a brilliant mechanism for collapsing the three dimensions of the ocean world—plus the fourth of time—into just two. Marhaver has explained this to me. Instead of sending the genetic material into the wide, three-dimensional ocean at random times, hoping the short-lived eggs will meet up with sperm from the same species and sperm will meet up with eggs, the corals send their bundles to the surface. That eliminates the whole dimension of depth. And they do it at the same moment. That eliminates the dimension of time. If some of the corals release their eggs and sperm at the wrong time or on the wrong day, they don't get to pass on their genetic material.

It's pretty smart strategy for an animal that can't walk or swim around to find a mate.

I wave my hands in front of me in the water. The plankton light up, bioluminescent. It's magical.

Then the fear swallows me up. I remember all that I don't know, can't yet understand about this water of life. Is there anything with long tentacles hanging near the surface? I sweep my light around. Then I remember that marine animals are attracted to light and switch it off. My mask fogs up. I'm not wearing my glasses—how far can I actually see? And I know that anything that could hurt me can swim a heck of a lot faster than I can.

The corals are not spawning. I'm ticking off the minutes. The divers below me are crowded around the transect, peering at the minute orifices of each coral polyp to see if they're ready. All at once, this seems slightly insane.

And in the end, nothing. No spawn.

Still, there are hopeful signs that something will happen in the next few days. The reef seems to know when the corals are about to spawn and other creatures spawn in response. And tonight they were sex crazy. The little brittle stars were standing up on tiptoes, arching their backs and spraying each other with sperm and big ruby-red eggs.

On day five only four corals spawn. No eggs are fertilised. Everyone is exhausted.

Day six and from the second Knowlton gets into the water, she knows that tonight is the night. The water is electric. Even land creatures like us can feel the sexual charge. It's as though the whole reef is vibrating.

It's 7:40 p.m. The first group of divers is already underwater, scouring the reef with high-powered flashlights, prepped with red glow sticks to mark anything interesting. At 7:43 Knowlton spots the first colony of corals getting ready to spawn.

Then, right on cue, it starts. The first bundle of eggs and sperm that the scientists are tracking heads up at 8:05, then another at 8:06, 8:08, two at 8:11, another at 8:12, 8:13, 8:14, 8:18 and then a couple of laggards at 8:21.

Divers follow them up, releasing red glow sticks to follow the bundles. That way, the two members of the team who are in a rowboat can follow the eggs and capture some of them in plankton nets. Later in the lab we'll look at them under the microscope to see what percentage is fertilised. It will give us a clue to how successful this year's spawn is.

I'm hanging on the surface again with my mask and snorkel. The air fills with a pungent salt funk. The whole reef is having sex. I can't see the bundles pop out but I can see them rise, pink and delicate, in the arc of my flashlight. And I can see the tiny creatures who are gorging on all this great egg and sperm protein. It's a feeding frenzy as much as a sexual one.

This is what all the reef organisms have been waiting for all year. It is a moment of exquisite hope.

Suddenly, though, there's lethargy. As if the reef is having a leisurely smoke at the end of it all.

The divers surface to change spent air tanks and plunge again. By 9:20 the other two coral species are 'setting'. At 9:46 the second spawn has begun and the surface fills again with ecto-plasm, the salt smell of sex and the eerie red light of the scientists' chemical glow sticks.

Finally, the spawn is done. Triumphantly we take our night's work to the lab, calling ourselves Team Spawn. We've gathered coral eggs. Now we have to wait to see whether they're fertilised and will start dividing into coral embryos. And, if so, what percentage.

By 4:15 a.m. hope is beginning to fade. Some years, every single egg sampled has been fertilised; tonight it's about half. Plus, team members—waterlogged and bleary-eyed—have added up the numbers and found that only about half the coral colonies that could have spawned did.

Biologically, these are not great odds. This ancient, magnificent rite of nature, so painstakingly catalogued tonight, has probably failed to produce enough baby corals.

On the other hand, in the whole long history of coral spawnings going back perhaps 450 million years, humans have witnessed and tried to catalogue just a few. Maybe in the grand scheme of things—in coral time—this is a pretty good spawn, given the bleaching and other exigencies.

Yet all these biologists gathered here at this research station know that the problems are larger than whether this particular spawn was successful. They know, for instance, that corals all over the Caribbean—and in many other seas—are in dire straits and declining in abundance. Scientists rarely see baby corals in the Caribbean any more, partly because the coral embryos that do make it through the spawn have trouble finding a clear spot on the sea floor to attach to. Without that, the embryos die.

They know that as the sea becomes more acidic, the corals are less able to use the calcium in it to make their bony mountains and that these delicate coral embryos might not survive in the more acidic water. They know that the corals are jeopardised by the pollution that pours off the fields and from the coastal towns into the shallow lagoons the corals need to survive, and by the rising water temperature that kills the microalgae the corals need to keep from starving.

Where will it end? And how? Can they recover? What does it mean if they don't?

When Knowlton became a marine biologist, it was for the thrill of understanding these extraordinary creatures. For Marhaver, Kline and Fogarty, it's a race to save them.

Down the hall, Dan Distell is preparing for the worst. For days now he's been following Team Spawn like a wraith, methodically collecting samples of the corals' genetic material for the Ocean Genome Legacy, a non-profit organisation based in Massachusetts. It's a biological contingency plan aimed at preserving genetic building blocks of marine life in case the animals and plants themselves stop being able to produce them. In other words, it's a small hedge against the corals' lack of fecundity. Distell has already confided to me that corals are a priority of the Ocean Genome Legacy because they are the most urgently endangered group of life known of in the world.

CHAPTER 6

READING THE VITAL SIGNS: LIFE FORCE

Halifax, Canada: The fate of the fish

Sometimes, in order to discern the present, you have to be able to see both the future and the past. Time has to be compressed into a single dimension, akin to folding a strip of indistinct photographic film into an accordion so that you can see many exposures layered on top of each other all at once and thus get a clear picture. If you lose the past, the present and the future cannot really be understood.

So it is with fish. If you don't know what used to be there, how can you judge what's there now, or what will be there over time?

This is one of the critical, obvious ways of measuring the health of the ocean, particularly since fish have been an integral part of the human food chain—and human consciousness—for thousands of years and have left traces through art, cookbooks, literature and garbage heaps. Until this generation of scientists, hardly anyone thought to try to discern fish trends, either in a specific part of the ocean or across the global ocean itself. This is a brave new field.

One of the most exciting universities in the world for this new field is Dalhousie in Halifax, on Canada's east coast. Here, marine biologists cut their teeth in the 1980s and 1990s on the legendary collapse of the Atlantic cod from overfishing in the sea outside their door.

They read the vital signs of that population, delivered the prognosis that the cod were in trouble from overfishing and were roundly ignored until the cod did, indeed, effectively vanish as a commercial and biological entity in that part of the sea. Even though cod fishing has been banned in that part of the ocean for more than fifteen years, the cod have failed to come back. It's not clear if or when they ever will. This biological conundrum has spawned much of the drive at Dalhousie to read the future of other fish.

The cod story points to another: the ocean's overall capacity to support life. Will other fish go the way of the cod? How will all the other changes in the global ocean—rising temperature, rising acidity, falling metabolism, dropping fecundity—interact with overfishing, and overfishing with them?

Could the global ocean ever really lose its ability to keep fish alive? And, if it did, how would that affect the other creatures that live in the sea, not to mention the billions of humans who rely on fish for food?

Three Dalhousie scientists are among those on the cutting edge of figuring out the future of fish and I've spoken to each of them many times. Their work is part of the global Census of Marine Life, which is trying to map what's in the ocean, what used to be in the ocean and what will be in the ocean over time.

Heike Lotze is an expert in reconstructing past marine and shore systems, in seeing what's no longer there. She grew up in the north of Germany, a few kilometres from the Wadden Sea, and has pioneered this type of biological detective work. Her work is fascinating because she goes through archaeological findings that tell of life thousands of years ago, and into poetry, medieval maps, art and prose to discern the types of marine animals and plants that were once there.

Boris Worm, who is married to Lotze, goes in precisely the opposite direction. He is a soothsayer, using complex mathematics and computer analysis to calculate present and predict future populations of fish in the sea.

This ecological forecasting is the work that he and Ransom Myers, the third Dalhousie scientist, have startled the world with over the past few years. Most notably, a few years ago they published a paper explaining that the populations of all the big predator fish in the ocean have plummeted by 90 per cent in the five decades or so since modern industrial fishing took hold. And the fish that remain don't grow nearly as large as they once did.

This paper—known as 'the 90-per-cent paper'—became so well known that it forms the basis for the public sense that something, somewhere is terribly wrong with the fishery. It's hit the public discourse far more powerfully than the problems with pH, oxygen or plankton. It's not as abstract.

More recently Worm, Lotze and a roster of colleagues from all over the world published the most controversial paper of all—Worm has taken to calling it 'the crazy paper' because there's been so much fallout—that predicted a full collapse by 2048 of all fish currently commercially caught, unless practices change.

This research paper has reached far past the narrow confines of scientific literature, even spawning mentions on late-night talk shows, in newspaper cartoons and in celebrity magazines.

Lotze and Worm are part of the young, fresh and brilliant new generation of marine biologists who are trained to synthesise information, to draw conclusions. Katharina Fabricius and Joanie Kleypas are part of the same crowd.

Myers, who's older than Lotze and Worm, is a legend in marine science around the world for his passion, quirkiness, vast influence and prolific work. Interviewing him is an exercise in shifting gears and speeding up. A few days before I am to arrive in Halifax,

I get an email from Lotze: Myers is in the hospital, diagnosed with malignant, inoperable brain cancer. It has happened catastrophically suddenly. The whole department, including the thirty graduate students Myers has been shepherding, is in mourning.

The story of humans and fish is the story of an explosion in the human population and the systematised extermination of fish.

Demographic analysis shows that the human population on this planet was about 300 million 2000 years ago at the beginning of the Common Era. A thousand years later, it was nearly the same at 310 million. A thousand years after that it was six billion. Terrible plagues such as HIV/AIDS notwithstanding, the earth's human population is still growing at 75 million a year.

Lotze, who holds the Canada Research Chair in Marine Renewable Resources, can catalogue how this has played out with fish over the centuries. It is a pattern of serial extinctions. When humans get to the end of one type of fish we move to another, depleting as we go, and moving from big, easy fish to smaller ones. We empty the streams, rivers and lakes, then the shores, then the sea and finally the open ocean, a trend that takes those who fish further and further from land and deeper under the surface of the sea.

When humans can't easily find wild fish we figure out how to farm them, as we did with carp in the Middle Ages and as we're doing now with Atlantic salmon in many parts of the world.

When I meet Lotze in her lab, she starts telling me about her studies of the Wadden Sea. It's one of just twelve sites across the world so far that have had a full historical work-up by Lotze and others using reconstructive detective techniques. Some of the others are Quoddy Bay on the eastern edge of Canada, Chesapeake Bay on the east coast of the United States, and San Francisco

Bay on the US Pacific coast. Of all these, the Wadden Sea has the best historical records.

The Wadden Sea—formed 7500 years ago when the Ice Age retreated and the sea rose—runs across part of the northern edge of Europe, flanking Denmark, Germany and the Netherlands. It is the world's largest intertidal system, a shoreline that is exposed at low tide. In addition, it is one of the world's most important coastal wetlands, which is why it's a candidate for designation as a World Heritage Site under the UNESCO program, an honour reserved for the planet's truly magnificent natural sites.

These two characteristics—the intertidal system and the coastal wetland—are a recipe for biological variety. The Wadden Sea is one of those margins between ecosystems where the land meets the water and they both meet the air. Life here can exist on many levels of the food chain at once, each feeding the other in a robust dance.

However, Lotze has discovered that, as rich as the Wadden Sea seems now, it was once almost unimaginably richer. Until about 1000 years ago it was a fabulous, interconnected system that was home to grey and right whales, porpoises, dolphins, seals, astounding three-dimensional oyster beds, eagles, pelicans, flamingos, egrets, herons and other huge birds. Massive cod, haddock, halibut and rays teemed in its waters, while metres-long salmon and sturgeon swam from river to sea.

Today the whales, including the greys that might once have had calving grounds in the Wadden Sea, have been extinct in this part of the ocean for centuries, hunted out of existence. Porpoises and dolphins are rarely seen. Grey and harbour seals are slowly coming back thanks to a reintroduction program in Britain.

Many of the big birds are now uncommon or have vanished altogether, killed off for eggs, feathers, down and flesh. Oysters with their huge, reef-like beds are almost extinct. Big fish have not been seen in rivers or the sea in many generations. Today, only three rivers in all of Europe still have sturgeon, once the favoured European fish that could grow to 400 kilograms.

As in so many other parts of the global ocean, whole, intricate communities of sea life are gone. Great swathes of the food web are no longer there, lost mainly at the top, and neither are key living spaces that once supported them, such as sea-grass beds and salt marshes.

What happened? The growing reach and sophistication of human society that began in the Middle Ages—including the burgeoning mercantile class, the growing population and the early Christian church—had an unprecedented impact on the surrounding natural world. During that time people began to eat not just what was handy, but also what was fashionable and what was allowed by the church. From about the fifth century, the Christian church forbade its faithful to eat 'flesh', or meat from land, on Fridays and holidays, about 130 days a year. In western Europe, including around the Wadden Sea, Christians were allowed to substitute fish—which meant anything that swam in water, including what we know as marine mammals—for meat on those days. They didn't like it. Meat from the land was much more palatable to them.

From the Neolithic period about 5000 years ago, after the hunter-gatherer era ended, the human settlers of the Wadden Sea area had eschewed ocean food in favour of food they could find or grow on the land. If they had to eat fish, as the church decreed, they vastly preferred fish from freshwater rather than the ocean.

Richard Hoffmann, a historian from York University in Toronto who works with Lotze, has examined garbage heaps, menus, kitchen accounts and other archaeological and historical evidence showing that Europeans before the twelfth century ate pike, sturgeon and salmon, all of which could be caught in streams nearby.

By the twelfth century, though, these same records show that people were eating fish from the sea. Freshwater fish, or fish such as salmon and sturgeon that lived at least part of the year in freshwater, were still cherished above ocean fare, but they were becoming more rare and more expensive. Eating them became a mark of prestige both in the world at large and within exclusive church circles. The rare pike, for example, became a favoured fish of European prelates. For most Europeans, these prized fish were out of reach.

Once the local fish, whether fresh or marine, were fished out, a commercial fishery evolved to supply the need. At first it was small; eventually it became the vast industrial fishery we know today.

In the Middle Ages, however, this infant industry sometimes involved selling the extra fish from a nobleman's lakes or shores. Sometimes it meant drying, salting or brining the fish so they could be sent, by transport, to markets a little further away.

Fishmongering became a profession, driven by local extinctions of wild fish and by the requirements of the church. Hoffman's research shows that by the eleventh and twelfth centuries, fish markets had become a key commodity in the new exchange market system that was beginning in Europe. His examples from France and England are illustrative of the phenomenon that was also developing near the Wadden Sea.

By the mid-thirteenth century, fast horses were taking marine fish from Normandy to Paris. Fifty years later, sea fish could be had even in central England, carried there by cart from English shores.

By the fifteenth century the fish trade had expanded even more. The streams of Normandy had no salmon left, so fishmongers there imported them from Scotland and Ireland in barrels of brine and sent them to Parisian tables.

From the sixteenth to the eighteenth centuries, cod, for one, vanished from the coastal seas around Europe, so intrepid fishermen went to Iceland to catch them, and eventually across the wide ocean to the banks of Newfoundland in the New World.

Sturgeon had become even rarer. Archaeological digs from the seventh to the ninth century in parts of Europe show that sturgeon made up about 70 per cent of the fish consumed by people. By the twelfth century sturgeon were nearly absent in streams from Italy to the Baltic. The few that could be found were small, no longer the 400-kilogram whoppers that once had swum the rivers of Europe. Cookbooks of the day offered recipes on how to make veal taste like sturgeon.

Eventually sturgeon became so rare that they were designated the 'royal fish', meaning that only royalty could consume them. Today, they're still endangered in most parts of Europe, and trade in sturgeon eggs—caviar, the modern luxury food—is tightly controlled.

Medieval Europeans not only made markets from wild fish when they couldn't catch them for their own use, they also made big business of farming fish; these were two key economic innovations of the age. By 1300 carp were being grown throughout Europe in large, man-made ponds. They were easy to rear, eating mainly garbage.

It wasn't just the fish and marine mammals that vanished from the Wadden Sea and the rivers that fed it. The living spaces of water creatures—and the birds that depended on them—were also systematically destroyed over time.

It began during the Bronze Age, after 1800 BCE, when farmers cut down trees along the sea's edge for lumber, fuel and fodder for their animals. By Roman times, near the beginning of the Common Era, the tidal forest of elm and ash was gone.

The Frisians, who settled on the Wadden Sea in the early Middle Ages, made an industry of salt. That involved digging up the tidal peat banks and the eelgrass beds, burning them and taking salt from the ashes. By the end of the Middle Ages, the tidal bogs had disappeared.

In the same era farmers began building strong dikes and drainage ditches to keep back the water for agriculture, essentially hand-making the landscape and getting rid of marshland. Residents of the area began harvesting sea grasses for mattresses and insulation, tearing up thousands of hectares of living structures of the ocean bed.

So the human inhabitants near the Wadden Sea fished or harvested much of the sea's life. They eliminated the places those creatures could inhabit if they returned. As a result, the ecosystem that remains is far less complex, with fewer layers of life. That makes what's left more vulnerable to other threats such as disease, higher temperatures and lower pH. But because these changes happened so long ago in that part of the world, they have passed from the local human memory.

'In North America, people remember the big fish,' Lotze tells me. 'In Europe, it's much harder. Flounder are only this big.' She holds her hands not very far apart. 'All the big fish are gone and somehow, nobody cares. People don't think they have an impact.'

Instead, humans seem to think they are removed from these fundamental cycles of the planet, especially the ocean, she says. In fact, the opposite is true. Everything we do every day is intimately connected with the ocean. As Worm puts it, every tear we shed ends up in the ocean, just as it originated there.

Lotze unrolls a huge, nine-panelled map of northern Europe and the surrounding waters made by the Swedish Catholic archbishop Olaus Magnus in 1539. He was a faithful naturalist and geographer, and this is the first detailed map ever produced of this area. It is a work of art, if not of unimpeachable science.

The map is also remarkable for the catalogue it provides of what the ocean meant to humans of that time and place. It gives a glimpse into how our modern ideas of the sea were born. And how we got to where we are now, both practically and philosophically.

To Olaus Magnus, the sea was full of monsters. Whales were fierce, featuring claws, dog-like teeth, green armour, double blow-holes and a lizard-like snout. Here, a giant lobster clutches a hapless man in its pincer. There, a fearsome crimson sea snake crushes a ship. A tusked, boar-like creature with flippers and a fish tail boasts three blood-red eyes on its torso. Storms swirl in the air; gyres bigger than the mythical maw of Charybdis suck ships into the deeps.

The ocean was a place of danger and death, outside the scope of the civilising force of humans. It was unpredictable, hellish, the unknown other; the enemy, a proxy for the unfathomable demons in the depths of the human soul. It was the opposite of safe places that humans carved out of nature and subdued to their will and their god.

In *Description of the Northern Peoples*, the book Olaus Magnus published in 1555 as a companion to the map, he goes even further, devoting a whole chapter to the horrors of monsters of the sea, in which he includes fish such as halibut and flounder, a sign of how large the fish of his era were. It's an archive of what's gone.

Today, Lotze says, the main commercial fishery the Wadden Sea is capable of supporting consists of shrimps and mussels. Even these are small.

Lotze and Worm are telling me about Ransom Myers. It's a painful subject. The cancer hit without warning and is in the part of his brain that controls how he can express himself. The part that can take information in is still working as brilliantly as ever, and possibly so is the part that can wring meaning out of information. But he can't tell anyone about it. He can say yes and no and sometimes one other word, but no more. It's clear to me that if I want him to tell me the future, I will have to read the oracle of the papers he has already published.

Because it happened so abruptly, Myers didn't have time to write down all the new analysis he had done, all the synthesis brewing in his brain. It's the nightmare of a scientist whose life's work was devoted to providing fair warning of dangers to come.

The loss is incalculable. He's one of the few marine biologists in the world capable of understanding what's happening with fish, and it's all locked in his head, a computer no one knows how to sort through.

It appears to be a metaphor for the fish he studies and so many of the other ecosystems of the sea: once something is lost, it can't be recovered. There is a point of no return.

Worm is a man under siege. He's just come from a lecture he gave to other scientists in his department on 'the crazy paper', capping about three months of patient, unceasing defence of this work.

It's the first major paper on the future of fish and it predicts, among other things, the total collapse of all commercial fisheries by 2048 unless practices change. It essentially gave a forty-year fair warning, dropped into a time when few realised there were deadlines at all, much less one so soon.

The paper, 'Impacts of biodiversity loss on ocean ecosystem services', published on 3 November 2006 in *Science*, vol. 314, pp. 787–790, spawned more than 100 newspaper editorials around the world, as well as a mention on Jay Leno's late-night television show.

Worm's departmental lecture today was friendly, because he works with people who are able to think in new ways about fish and who believe that this type of paper is a worthy first stab at a phenomenally complex subject.

Others have not been so supportive. The paper has been bitterly, emotionally contested in scientific circles. The critics have been fisheries scientists and the supporters have been marine ecologists. *Science* has published attacks from other fisheries researchers and rebuttals by the paper's authors. Because Worm is the first author listed on the paper, he has taken most of the flak.

He's unrepentant. He's been telling me that as a boy growing up in Germany he was crazy for maps, an explorer at heart. I think that's why he enjoys swimming against the scientific current if he believes the current is flowing the wrong way: it's part of his own intellectual exploration.

Worm is the unusual sort of scientist who believes in helping people challenge their assumptions. In his conservation biology class, for example, he makes a practice of asking a biological question to which there is no known answer, and then getting his students to research it and write papers on it.

On the wall across from his desk at the university he has posted several of his favourite newspaper cartoons, each based on one of his articles. One shows an old man talking to a child, saying wistfully, 'In my day, we used to eat fish with our chips.' Another features a museum exhibiting three extinct animals: a woolly mammoth, a dinosaur and a fish. A third shows a fish on a psychiatrist's couch and the doctor saying: 'It's not your imagination . . . The whole world *is* out to get you.'

The impact of the paper's forty-year warning doesn't seem to wane. While we're talking Worm gets a phone call from a researcher at *Vanity Fair*, the celebrity magazine. He's never even read it. They want him to help them put together some information on fish trends. He tells them yes and gets off the phone, shaking his head. Later I pick him up a copy of the latest issue and he laughs uproariously as he leafs through the stories of fashion, celebrity and easy wealth. They have so little in common with his life.

In fact, 'the crazy paper' did much more than put a deadline on the salvation of fish. The figure 2048 was almost a footnote, tossed in to highlight the urgency of changing fishing practices.

The larger message of the research is that the global ocean, as a whole functioning system, provides important services to humanity, such as protection from floods, removing the toxins from waste, and serving up food. (The authors don't look at carbon and oxygen cycles.) As humans remove different types of life from the ocean's food web, we impair the ability of the global ocean to provide those services. And, therefore, to keep itself healthy.

For example, fishing out whole species and then whole families of sea life makes the life that remains far less likely to thrive. The more types of life there are in a given part of the global ocean, the healthier that part of the ocean is, and the more likely it is to be able to provide food and other services to humanity.

In other words, the complex, planet-supporting ocean system that humans are just starting to understand has evolved to work in balance. When humans remove great swathes of species from the mix, things don't work the same way. The symbiosis of species and chemistry changes. The system becomes vulnerable.

Fish whose populations have been fished out don't come back easily to their original numbers. Floodplains and salt marshes that have been destroyed can't filter the toxins from water, and that leads to more toxic algal blooms, fish kills, beach closures and low oxygen in the water.

'The crazy paper' builds on the infamous '90-per-cent paper' that Worm and Myers published in *Nature* on 15 May 2003 (vol. 423, pp. 280–283), which in turn builds on Lotze's work about historical damage to the structure of coastal ecosystems.

While Lotze's work looks at specific places where the ocean meets the land over time, 'the 90-per-cent paper' looks at commercial catches around the world since large-scale, intensive industrial fishing began in the 1950s, both at continental shelves and in the open ocean.

One of the main fishing mechanisms through this time was long-line fishing, which involves setting hooks at regular intervals across vast areas of the ocean. That means it's possible to compare over time how many fish are caught for every 100 hooks. Figures from the open ocean come from Japanese fishing fleets from 1952 to 1999, because Japan had the most widespread long-line fishing operation, extending to all oceans except those at the poles.

The findings are astonishingly consistent. During the first few years that a new type of fish is targeted, catch rates are very high. A few years in, the catches plummet.

In the Gulf of Thailand, for example, 60 per cent of large fish with fins, sharks and skates were taken from the ocean in the first five years of industrial fishing. In the narrow shelf of South Georgia in the southern Atlantic Ocean, fish stocks were depleted in the first two years.

On average, 80 per cent of the populations of fish had vanished within fifteen years of the start of industrial activity. As Worm and Myers point out, that's often before any scientific monitoring takes place, which means that by the time the scientists get there to try to figure out how much fishing should proceed, they've already missed the proverbial boat. They're trying to maintain populations of fish at what are already historically low levels. It doesn't leave much room for error.

In all, Worm and Myers calculate that the populations of every single large predatory fish across the global ocean fell by 90 per cent in the fifty years after industrialised fishing began.

As fishing became more difficult, other studies show that fishermen began spending both more time and more money to catch fewer fish, using sophisticated, expensive sonar and satellite equipment to target their catch. As well, they began to go yet deeper into the ocean and lower on the food chain. It's a recipe for trying to catch the very last fish.

Catches of deep-water creatures—mainly deep-ocean squid—jumped by more than 20 per cent between 2002 and 2004, according to figures from the Food and Agriculture Organisation of the

United Nations (FAO). One of Myers's PhD students, Peter Ward, has found that the commercial fishery now routinely goes to 400 to 500 metres, about double the depth they went to in 1953.

Moreover, a study published in 2006 in *Nature* showed that populations of fish that live in deep northwest Atlantic waters were decimated in just seventeen years once commercial outfits targeted them, leaving anywhere from 11 per cent to just 2 per cent of the fish.

·   Another study, by Daniel Pauly of the University of British Columbia and others, has calculated that the world's total fish catch peaked in the mid-1980s and has since declined. An estimated fifth of all the fish caught and killed in US waters are thrown back into the sea because they're the wrong type. In other countries, that could be higher.

Pauly and his research group have also shown that fishing fleets around the world are using up ever more fossil fuels as they travel further to catch fewer fish, one of the few major industries on the planet that is using more energy to conduct its business rather than less.

In all, studies have found that the commercial fishery consumes 1.2 per cent of the oil used around the globe every year, running through more than twelve times as much energy to catch fish as the fish themselves provide in food energy to those who consume them.

How do fishermen pay for all this energy, equipment and time? A study published in 2006 by Pauly and his colleague Rashid Sumaila shows that government subsidies to the global fishery came in at between US$30 billion and $34 billion, including a substantial portion to offset the costs of fuel. Just as a point of comparison, Sumaila calculates that the total value of all fish caught in 2000 was about US$80 billion.

The modern trends show the same picture that Lotze's research found at the thinned-out ecosystems where the ocean meets the land in the Middle Ages. First, fishermen go further out to sea to find the fish; then they switch to a species lower on the food chain; then they increase the technological level of their fishing gear while also expending more effort to catch fewer fish; finally, they turn to farming fish.

FAO figures show that in 2004 about a third of the fish humans ate came from farms, up from about 4 per cent in 1970. That proportion is growing year by year as the wild fishery declines and becomes more difficult to fish. During roughly the same fifty-year period that Worm and Myers examined in their '90-per-cent paper', aquaculture production in the world rose from less than 1 million tonnes to nearly 60 million tonnes. Aquaculture is growing far more rapidly across the world than all other types of animal farming.

In a cruel irony, one of the staples of aquaculture is small wild-caught fish, which are ground up and made into meal to feed the captive creatures. It takes 2.5 kilograms of ground-up herring to produce 1 kilogram of farmed salmon, Lotze has told me. On the bright side, that's down from the 4 kilograms of herring needed to produce the same kilogram of salmon in 1980.

What are the implications of all that Worm, Myers and Lotze have found?

Worm takes the synoptic view. It took humans roughly 50,000 years to deplete the planet's large land animals, 5000 years to exhaust most of the planet's coastal environments, 500 years to fish out the continental shelf, 50 years to impoverish the open ocean and about 5 years to run through the creatures of the deep ocean.

'We don't realise how absolutely exceptional this time is. We are reaching the carrying capacity of the planet's natural resources,' he says, adding: 'We are at the stage of losing the ability of things to come back on their own.' He pauses, then says carefully, looking me straight in the eyes: 'That would represent a threshold.'

I've just come from a PhD thesis defence with Worm and all I can think about is apoptosis. The defence, by Ward, one of Myers's graduate students, was a roaring success. Ward can now officially call himself Dr Peter Ward. He's jubilant. But as triumphant as his day was, it was also poignant. Myers, as Ward's supervisor and co-author on several papers, ought to have been there, doing his usual schtick of appearing to pay no attention, banging on his computer keyboard and then surfacing to ask the most piercing question of all.

In spirit, Myers was there: one of his other students was there videotaping the whole event to show to Myers in the hospital.

Ward has carried on Myers's work of gauging present fish populations in the global ocean compared to fifty years ago when industrial fishing began. His research shows catastrophic declines across all commercial species of fish and the fish that remain are far smaller than historic norms.

Five chapters of his thesis have already been published as peer-reviewed journal articles and a sixth has been accepted for publication. Ward is already an established scientist working on some of the most critical questions humanity is facing.

He's got the battle scars to prove it. He routinely gets reamed out at international fishery meetings, he says, describing himself as 'battered and bruised'. It baffles him. He's trying to explain to the world community how many fish were there fifty years ago and, therefore, how fishery catch models need to change to reflect that, so modern catches can be sustained. But he is told time and time again that his data have to be ignored because they don't fit the model.

Who makes the fish-catch model? Who knows. It's a black box, he says. He thinks it should be opened.

'We've never exploited these fish to this level and we don't know what happens next,' he tells the defence committee.

So how does apoptosis fit in? It's a cancer metaphor: cells in healthy bodies are programmed to kill themselves if they are damaged beyond repair, starving, poisoned or diseased. When a cell gets to the point of no return, instead of trying to stay alive, it switches into apoptosis mode and dies so it can be replaced by another, healthy cell.

It makes sense. The healthy body must continually make new cells—about 50 to seventy billion a day in adult humans—to replace damaged ones. But the body needs to stay in balance—in homeostasis. So for every new cell required, an old cell must die. That's how the body stays within the narrow range of what's biologically possible. Otherwise you might get humans with huge hands or an enormous spine or one exceptionally large lung. It's how the body stays healthy and recycles the useful components of its cells. It's similar to other inexorable cycles of biology: death leads to life leads inevitably to death. Winter must be followed by spring. Time is a loop, not a line.

In many forms of cancer, a sick cell's ability to self-destruct is absent. It refuses to die, replicating instead along with the disease. That's the definition of a tumour. Apoptosis, therefore, is both good and necessary.

This is another way to understand what's happening to the global ocean system. The ocean system's chemistry is changing in ways not known for at least twenty million years; its life forms are being demolished at an unprecedented rate with unknown consequences; its fecundity is in question and so is its metabolic rate. It faces far more assaults in the coming decades from yet more carbon dioxide, physical destruction and over-fishing unless human behaviour changes dramatically. The vital signs are not good.

Is this the story of the ocean nudging toward apoptosis—dying, leaving the old system with its destructive humans behind so it can create something new? Except not a single cell as in cancer, but a whole complex system?

I go back to Worm. He is resolutely hopeful that humanity can change its destructive patterns. We can, he avers, learn from the past. He, Lotze, Myers and many other scientists have put that belief at the core of their lives. It's why they study the things they do.

Part of the problem now, he says, is that what's happening in the ocean is hidden from the public. People don't know what's at stake. Take fishery catches, for example—why are we continuing to fish too much? Who's in charge?

The answer is that nobody knows. A handful of unknown, invisible people are making these decisions that affect the biological fate of the global ocean, if not the planet. They are not public figures. They do not have to explain their decisions or defend them against public inquiry. They don't even tell the public what their decisions are. It's not much of a model. And it's plainly not working for the long haul.

Worm points to a better model, one that Myers used to praise lavishly. It dates back to 2 December 1946—the International Convention for the Regulation of Whaling. Established because all species of whales were in danger from, as the convention says, 'overfishing of one area after another and of one species of whale after another to such a degree that it is essential to protect all species of whales from further overfishing', the convention has succeeded in preventing the extinction of all species of whale and in increasing their populations.

Whales came to be seen as a global 'great natural resource' that needed to be protected for future generations. So a committee meets to decide whether any whales will be hunted and, if so, how many. The decisions are made public and debated. Data on how the decisions are working are also public, as are trends in whale populations.

The Convention on International Trade in Endangered Species of Wild Fauna and Flora, known as CITES and brought into international force in 1973, has been, as Worm puts it '100 per cent successful'. It regulates the trade of animals and plants that are known to be in biological danger so that their populations remain healthy. Nothing put on the list has become extinct. Again, its meetings are reported on and so are its decisions.

Worm also points to other environmental solutions that have been implemented over the years, including controlling coal pollution in cities, DDT, PCBs and dioxins. There has also been a successful international pact in 1987 to ban the use of ozone-depleting substances.

In Worm's home continent, Europe, there are now carpets of wind farms producing energy to replace fossil fuels. The land where Lotze grew up on the Wadden Sea has been turned into a solar energy farm by her sister's husband, a livelihood none of the earlier generations of farmers and fishermen who lived there over the millennia would have dreamed of.

'I'm absolutely hopeful,' Worm says. 'I would be suicidal if I weren't hopeful.'

Lotze and Worm drive a hybrid car and have converted their home overlooking the Atlantic Ocean so that it draws heat from the sun and water from the roof. I've noticed that for lunch they eat home-made mackerel sandwiches—low on the fish food ladder—and that Lotze continually has half packets of sugar in her pockets, left over from her cups of coffee because she can neither bear to use the full packet nor throw out the half. They are the smart new generation, both as scientists and as citizens. They have learned from the past and have retained hope. They have taught themselves to ask the questions that don't have easy answers.

Just as much as the fish they study, they are part of the life force of the future ocean. They have the ability to understand the ocean's secrets and tell us about them, to give us fair warning.

The month after I leave Halifax, I read in a newspaper that Myers has died.

CHAPTER 7

READING THE VITAL SIGNS: MEDICAL HISTORY

Spain: The last time the sea was sick

The earth is a jealous guardian of her tales. She lays them down with exquisite precision and then hides them, building an archive only to lock it away. Finding the key is an uncertain business, dependent as much on chance as design. And being able to read the tales themselves—the secrets of the earth's past—if they are found takes yet more serendipity and skill.

A case in point is the elusive fossil marker from fifty-five million years ago, when the planet's atmosphere heated up dramatically. It strikes scientists that this is a parallel to what's happening in today's world. This marker is the PETM, for Paleocene-Eocene Thermal Maximum, named after the geological epochs that bracket it. A global crisis, it affected the planet's systems throughout land and sea, and only in the past decade have scientists begun to understand the lessons contained within this slice of the fossil record. To them it has become the Rosetta stone of global climate change; the best—if not perfect—analogue they have for what's happening today.

It is another vital sign that will help explain the significance of what's happening in today's global ocean. Put another way: what happened last time the planet was sick in this way?

So I find myself climbing the Pyrenees on a rainy morning in the north of Spain, in search of the PETM. There have been four days' worth of cutting-edge scientific papers on the phenomenon and now I want to put my hands on it, bear witness to what it means.

This is the field trip portion of a select international conference, Climate and Biota of the Early Paleogene, held every three years or so for the palaeontologists and climate scientists who are studying this deeply hidden piece of history.

Henk Brinkhuis and Appy Sluijs, two palaeoecologists at the University of Utrecht in the Netherlands, are the conference's current superstars because a few weeks ago they scored the cover article in *Nature* and hundreds of media hits around the world on their analysis of core samples from the deep Arctic, which showed for the first time just how warm the northern sea was.

Many of the other papers we have been listening to in an auditorium in Bilbao are also destined to shake up our view of the world. This is a preview of the science headlines to come, and, as best as anyone can tell, of the future itself.

So what exactly happened during the PETM? It was already warm, unlike today, when the planet is in a cool phase of its existence. The carbon dioxide concentration of the atmosphere was already high, estimated at anywhere from 600 to as much as 2800 parts per million (ppm). Today, by contrast, the concentration is about 387 ppm, up from about 280 ppm before the mass burning of fossil fuels began a quarter millennium ago. The concentration has remained below 300 ppm for at least twenty million years.

In that hothouse fifty-five million years ago an almost unimaginable amount of carbon was released into the atmosphere and ocean all at once. It happened in a geological instant, or between one and about 1000 years. The amount was equivalent to just over a doubling of the atmospheric carbon dioxide concentrations. In chemical composition, this carbon burp was similar to the residue from burned oil, gas and coal. The carbon and oxygen isotopes contained in the fossils from this period tell the story.

First, though, a chemistry primer, using carbon as an example. Carbon is one of the 117 (so far) natural and synthetic chemical elements that exist on earth. All atoms of carbon contain six protons, giving it the atomic number six on the periodic table. This is invariable. But each atom also has an atomic mass, or weight, which is the sum of its protons and neutrons. Most elements naturally have varying atomic weights, meaning that the atoms have varying numbers of neutrons. These atoms of different weights are the isotopes of an element. Carbon can have six, seven or eight neutrons. This means its atomic weight is either 12 (six protons + six neutrons), 13 (six protons + seven neutrons) or 14 (six protons + eight neutrons). The isotope carbon-12 is lighter than carbon-13 because its atomic weight is lower.

In a nutshell, when there's a tremendous amount of carbon in the atmosphere, plants and animals use the light carbon isotope, leaving behind the heavy; it's the path of least resistance. When fossils show more than the usual proportion of light carbon isotopes, rather than the classical balance of light and heavy, it means carbon was superabundant.

Fossils from the PETM—whether from land or sea—show a stunning spike of the light isotope. The spike is known as a carbon isotopic excursion.

The spike fifty-five million years ago is so sharp that it represents as much carbon as if every living thing on land or in the sea had been instantly incinerated. The key is not just the extraordinary amount of carbon—more than doubling carbon dioxide concentrations in the atmosphere—but also the speed with which it entered the planetary cycle. It happened too fast for much of the living earth to adapt. The system that had existed was overwhelmed, pushed past its limits, and a new system was born.

From the tropics to the poles, the surface air temperature rose by at least 5 degrees Celsius in less than 10,000 years, a catastrophic rise over a geologically short period.

The ocean suffered its own chemical catastrophe. The carbonate compensation depth—meaning the level below which calcium carbonate dissolves in the ocean—rose dramatically, a sign that the ocean's acidity also spiked through an influx of dissolved carbon dioxide from the atmosphere.

Several of the ocean's currents stopped or shifted course and the sea level rose. The coral reefs of the ancient Tethys Sea— which later, as the continents and tectonic plates shifted across the surface of the planet, became the Mediterranean and gave birth to the Atlantic Ocean—died off, replaced first by algae-slicked coral reef structures and then by brand new, large species of the primitive marine organisms called foraminifera.

The deep sea itself, which scientists until recent generations had believed to be immune from big changes, warmed by 4 or 5 degrees Celsius and so did the surface temperatures of the hurricane-prone waters in the tropics. Dinoflagellates, a common type of marine plankton, spread from their normal subtropical waters further north and south in concert with the warmer waters. As the Dutch scientists Brinkhuis and Sluijs discovered, the Arctic became like a giant warm bathtub with a freshwater lid. Surface sea waters there warmed up by 9 or 10 degrees Celsius and were thick with fast-growing freshwater ferns.

Temperatures in the middle of the big continents of the era (which were different from those of today, as was the configuration of the global ocean) rose by an average of 5 degrees Celsius. In the lands of the tropical rainforests, annual average temperatures hit as much as 34 degrees Celsius. The threshold for plant death in those areas is 33 degrees Celsius. One study showed that roughly three-quarters of the Columbian rainforest died.

The planet was sweltering. It rained copiously. In the fossil record here in the Iberian Peninsula there is evidence of extreme flooding, ferocious storms and frequent cyclones and those patterns may have been present elsewhere.

Across the planet, wherever palaeontologists look, whether on the bottom of the ocean or on land, they see extinctions of creatures that had been hardy enough to have survived the chaos that had killed the dinosaurs and so many other living things ten million years earlier. For example, as many as half the species of ocean-bottom dwelling foraminifera, one-celled creatures with chambered shells, suddenly became extinct right across the globe while other, larger foraminifera appeared for the first time.

Lots of new creatures abruptly came into being, often miniature versions of species that had been plentiful before the great warming. It was, eventually, a splendid time for mammals, which proliferated and shifted into many new forms, moving across the continents to parts of the world that had been inhospitable to them before.

Palaeontologists reckon it was roughly 150,000 years before the climate and ocean returned to the way they had been. Meaning, the PETM was not only intense and abrupt climate change but also sustained.

There's another element to the PETM that could be instructive in looking at the planet's vital signs. It's not just that the PETM carries the stigmata of intense global climate change, or that it is an eerie confirmation of the warnings that former US Vice President Al Gore, Australian biologist Tim Flannery and much of the scientific community have been sounding—it's also that the PETM shows the part of the coming picture that is scarier than these warnings. Changes as vast as those now affecting the atmosphere and ocean are not linear. They feed on themselves and grow exponentially, reaching a point at which the system switches abruptly to one that is dramatically different.

Observers of the modern climate system are already seeing signs that things are moving unbelievably rapidly, to an extent surprising even to the scientists. For example, the scientists in charge of predicting how fast the permanent ice is melting in today's Arctic are having trouble keeping their presentations up to date because the melting is running so far ahead of predictions.

Fifteen years ago there was talk of an ice-free Arctic in the summers by 2100. Seven years ago scientists reckoned it would happen by 2050. In 2007 a Russian ship made it through the Northwest Passage in September, when traditionally the ice is fast. Now, scientists are seriously examining whether the passage will be open all summer in just a few years.

At the same time, human emissions of greenhouse gases are increasing far ahead of calculations, as if they are feeding on themselves. A recent paper showed that while emissions rose at an average of 1.3 per cent a year through the 1990s, by the first half of this decade (from 2000 to 2006), they rose by 3.3 per cent a year on average. In part this is because the land and the ocean, which have been soaking up carbon dioxide, are getting saturated.

About five years ago analysts were predicting that China would become the world's largest emitter of carbon dioxide anywhere from 2015 to 2020. In fact, that happened in 2006 when, for the first time, China outpaced the United States in emissions. This means that the global economy, of which China is a major driver, is growing faster than expected, sending ever more emissions into the atmosphere and ocean.

Even if we stopped emitting greenhouses gases today, there is already so much carbon in the atmosphere that the average temperature would continue to rise by a tenth of a degree Celsius every decade for a century.

The latest report from the Intergovernmental Panel on Climate Change (IPCC)—the blue-ribbon report that all countries have to agree on before it can be published—has estimated that when the concentration gets to 450 ppm, which now seems both inevitable and imminent, the average surface air temperature will rise by about 2 degrees Celsius, and that will mean the extinction of from 20 per cent to 40 per cent of existing species on earth, which is a catastrophic number.

Many analysts say that humans will not stop at 450 but, rather, will push the concentration to 550 ppm, which is close to that critical point of a quick doubling of the concentration before industrialisation. At that point the average temperature will have risen by 3 degrees Celsius and as many as 70 per cent of the planet's species will have become extinct. That level of extinction has happened only five times before in the planet's history. The last time was when the dinosaurs died off sixty-five million years ago.

This is the portrait of a system poised to fall off a cliff.

The PETM looks unremarkable when I finally see it. We are at the Lizarraga Pass in the wild Pyrenees, part of the Navarre. The fog is heavy here and it feels chilly after the wall of wet heat in Bilbao. Horses are strolling up a mountain path, nosing out favourite grasses; bells strung around their necks tinkle. Colts play. Over there a clutch of black sheep gaze down at us.

And here is the PETM. To me it looks exactly like everything else I'm seeing: just dirt. No obvious fossils, no rocks, nothing to distinguish it from anything else. Nothing I can make out to tell where it begins or ends. But to these geologists and palaeontologists, this is a gold mine. They swarm it, pulling out hammers and magnifying lenses, and start hacking away, collecting pieces that they carefully label to take back to the laboratories of Europe and America.

Fifty-five million years ago, this was where the land met the sea, explains Robert Speijer, a geologist at the Catholic University in Leuven, Belgium who, along with Christopher Hollis, a New

Zealand micropalaeontologist, has agreed to explain the field-trip science to me as we go. Speijer is the expert on the dismal fate of the coral reefs of the ancient Tethys Sea.

When the movement of tectonic plates forced the Iberian Peninsula to crash up against Europe, all these geological records came to the surface from deep below, creating the Pyrenees. Thanks to that, and the sheep farmers who cleared the forests from this land in the Middle Ages, this part of the record is now visible but undisturbed for all these millions of years so scientists can tell its age.

'This is the Palaeocene,' Speijer says, pointing to the fossil record on the other side of the dirt in question. 'And that is certainly Eocene.' He points the other way, to a slice of earth that looks roughly the same.

This means the chunk in the middle has to be at the border between the two epochs, meaning it holds the stories of the warming that have so much to tell us about the fate of our own world. It is not quite 2 metres high.

However, Speijer and the others are not willing to assign provenance to the PETM without running a lot more tests on it. Thus the samples. They will take these clear plastic bags home, dry out the samples and extract microscopic marine fossils from them. After that they will try to identify these minuscule fossils by species and, hopefully, find the isotopic pattern that will show that they lived and died during the PETM.

Speijer hands me his hammer and gestures to the seam of dirt where the other geologists are working. I climb over and bang off a piece of it. When I pick it up, it is soft and wet. It crumbles a little in my hands. I cradle it in my palms, thinking of the incantatory power of the archive I am holding, the mysteries it can reveal.

When I show it to Speijer, he expertly breaks it into pieces, looking for signs of the fossils of ancient foraminifera, or forams, as they're called in shorthand. The sample crumbles through his fingers and falls to the ground, now just dust to dust.

It has not been a secret that the climate might change abruptly. Scientists have tried, however ineffectually, to explain it to the public for several years. Their findings have failed to capture the collective imagination. The public, politicians and journalists seem indifferent to the hazards of failing to take abrupt climate change into account.

Or, perhaps, it is hubris, that unlovely human characteristic, that has caused us to fail to think about what the coming climate change will mean for humanity. We have, it seems to me, harboured the necessary fiction that somehow human ingenuity will make everything all right, that we are destined to survive, that we will pull a technological rabbit out of the hat.

As far back as 2001 the report from the Intergovernmental Panel on Climate Change warned about abrupt climate change. Looking back now, I see that in its own jargony way it was strongly worded, if not starred and underlined. Scientists rarely deal in absolutes. They are trained to figure out which other questions to ask. It was easy for the public and politicians to misinterpret the words as being less serious than scientists intended.

This is from the summary document: 'Greenhouse gas forcing in the 21st century could set in motion large-scale, high-impact, non-linear, and potentially abrupt changes in physical and biological systems over the coming decades to millennia, with a wide range of associated likelihoods.

'Some of the projected abrupt/non-linear changes in physical systems and in the natural sources and sinks of greenhouse gases could be irreversible, but there is an incomplete understanding of some of the underlying processes.'

That was alarming enough for some scientists to press for further investigation. In the US the National Research Council set up a committee on abrupt climate change, which came out with a report in 2002 entitled *Abrupt Climate Change: Inevitable Surprises*. The report seizes on a single idea, the 'surprising new findings that abrupt climate change can occur when gradual causes push the earth system across a threshold.' It's the proverbial straw that breaks the camel's back. At that point, the climate sets off on its own path, at its own pace.

The report's conclusion: 'Large, abrupt climate changes have repeatedly affected much or all of the earth, locally reaching as much as 10 [degrees Celsius] in ten years. Available evidence suggests that abrupt climate changes are not only possible but likely in the future, potentially with large impacts on ecosystems and societies.'

By 2003 that scenario had prompted the Pentagon in the US to commission a report on the implications of abrupt climate change on national security. Dated October 2003, the report, *An Abrupt Climate Change Scenario and Its Implications for United States National Security* by Peter Schwartz and Doug Randall, focuses on what would happen if the Gulf Stream, which transports heat from the equator to the North Atlantic Ocean, shut off.

The report predicted shortages of food, water and energy that 'could potentially de-stabilize the geo-political environment, leading to skirmishes, battles, and even war . . . Unlikely alliances could be formed as defense priorities shift and the goal is resources for survival rather than religion, ideology, or national honor.'

The report is, at essence, a plea for permission to plan for anarchy. Could this really happen? the report asked.

The answer followed: 'Ocean, land, and atmosphere scientists at some of the world's most prestigious organizations have uncovered new evidence over the past decade suggesting that the plausibility of severe and rapid climate change is higher than most of the scientific community and perhaps all of the political community is prepared for.

'If it occurs, this phenomenon will disrupt current gradual global warming trends, adding to climate complexity and lack of predictability. And paleoclimatic evidence suggests that such an abrupt climate change could begin in the near future.'

A beautiful irony is built into these reports. The specific piece of the climate picture that spawned them is the rapid melting of the Arctic ice from global climate warming. That phenomenon is pouring freshwater into the top of the Atlantic Ocean, forcing its salt levels to drop. Less salty water is lighter than heavily salted water and doesn't sink as easily deep into the ocean. That means it affects the vast conveyor belt, known as the Gulf Stream or the Greenland pump, that carries heat from the equator to points north.

Ice core samples from Greenland show that the conveyor belt shut off 12,700 years ago during an event called the Younger Dryas and then again 8200 years ago. The theory is that if it shuts off again, the ocean heat that keeps northern Europe warm will stay south, plunging England and parts of Europe into a cold spell. The conveyor belt is thought to be so critical to the planet's climate system that it has been dubbed its 'Achilles' heel'.

This is the scenario taken to its extreme in the 2004 Hollywood movie *The Day After Tomorrow*. It showed a snap ice age in North America, complete with an ice-bound Statue of Liberty and valiant Americans freezing to death in their steps.

While the Gulf Stream has indeed shut down before and is likely on its way to doing so again—there is plenty of evidence that the salinity of the North Atlantic is dropping sharply and rising in other parts of the global ocean—many scientists now believe this has been a red herring, drawing attention and research from far graver and more immediate threats. In fact, it's been called the equivalent of an urban legend.

Matt Huber of Purdue University in Indiana, one of the world's top climate modellers, is helping me sort through the significance of the conference's scientific papers while we're in Bilbao. He says that most climate models show that winds drive the heat circulation, not the Gulf Stream conveyor belt. That's why, for example, Juneau in Alaska is relatively balmy despite the lack of a similar ocean conveyor belt in the Pacific Ocean.

'The theoretical problem is that when you measure how much heat is transported [through the Gulf Stream] past 60 degrees north, it's indistinguishable from zero,' Huber says.

The irony is that while the Gulf Stream issue focused the attention of at least some policymakers—to what degree it's not clear—and put the concept of abrupt climate and ocean change at least on the fringes of the map, it happened before the arrival of the really worrying new evidence about the phenomenon as a whole. That's the evidence just now emerging from these microfossils of the PETM.

A key question is: where did the PETM's massive infusion of carbon come from?

One of the leading theories is that the carbon exploded in a gaseous burp from the ocean floor when methane hydrates stored there—as they are now—somehow broke free. It reminds me of all that methane sitting now at the bottom of the Arabian Sea and the concerns of Peter Burkill of Plymouth that they will breach the surface.

Huber explains that methane hydrates, when cold, are like geodesic domes lying stable in the ocean's deeps. But the bonds holding the molecules together are fragile. If they are shaken up or warmed, the bonds break and bubbles of highly flammable methane (which is a carbon compound and a highly efficient greenhouse gas) shoot through the water column at phenomenal speed.

If that happened on a large enough scale throughout the ocean floor, intense global warming would happen instantly, Huber says. A possible trigger for the methane burp could be that the deep ocean warmed by perhaps a couple of degrees. It could have been a landslide that ripped up the slopes of the ocean basin and shook up the methane hydrates.

Or the carbon could have come from somewhere else.

Mark Pagani, of Yale University's Department of Geology and Geophysics, is an expert on historic carbon concentrations in the atmosphere, and he doesn't buy the methane theory. He says it was appealing a few years ago but, like a lover whose time has passed, should now be discarded.

'It was a very sexy idea and it's had its day,' he tells me.

One of the problems is that it is not known what volume of methane hydrates existed in the oceans of fifty-five million years ago. Was there enough to spark the kind of warming that the fossil record clearly shows?

Another issue is that the type of carbon contained in methane would warm up the world far more quickly than carbon dioxide, but would last only about a dozen years in the atmosphere until it transformed into carbon dioxide. The PETM lasted around 150,000 years.

Today, the isotopic signature of most of the extra carbon in the atmosphere shows that it comes from the burning of fossil fuels. In addition, as humans fell forests and till the soil, some of the landscapes that once absorbed carbon can't do that any more.

'We don't know what the final result of this is going to be,' says Pagani. 'We don't know the consequences of our actions. The thing about the climate system is, it's a monster. Once it shifts, it's not going to shift back.'

He pauses to think for a moment. Then, as if to scotch any sense I have that he's alarmist, he adds, 'I'm not willing to say it's going to be bad. It's going to be different.' He pauses one more beat: 'Florida will be gone.'

So where will it end up? And when? And how will *Homo sapiens* fare?

Huber, as the ranking climate modeller at this conference, is the professional seer of the future. While some of the scientists here are talking about catastrophe within fifteen years, Huber is comfortable talking about the next forty-five.

So, sure, he's worried about the methane hydrates, the possibility of a permanent El Niño weather pattern that will turn the Amazon rainforest into a desert and give us an open Northwest Passage. He's heard other scientists talk about New York as New Atlantis, about Bangladesh submerged. Privately he figures that the human population is going to take a hit, but he'll only say it will happen 'in the next thousand years'.

'I don't see us getting away with any less than a very large population downturn,' he says.

What's really disturbing him right now, though, is his theory about cyclones. The way he sees it, tropical cyclones are one of the mechanisms nature has developed to mix the hot waters on the surface of the ocean with cooler waters underneath. As they mix they move, ferrying the heat to new parts of the planet.

Mean sea surface temperatures in tropical oceans have risen about a quarter of a degree Celsius in recent years. The intensity of cyclones has doubled at the same time. His models predict that tropical sea surfaces will warm up by 2.5 degrees Celsius over the next century. Implications for the intensity of hurricanes are enough to make his upper lip sweat.

He can see how cyclones of this magnitude could explain some of the strange phenomena of the PETM, including the fact that some parts of the fossil record look like violent dumps of sediment. And hurricanes of this magnitude are not now represented in any climate models, past, present or future.

Peter Wilf, a geologist at Penn State University, has other concerns as well. At the PETM, the globe was already warm. The creatures then alive had evolved in warm conditions. Today, as carbon gets pumped so furiously into the atmosphere, we are in a relatively cool period of the earth's history. And the creatures alive today—including humans—are used to a cool regime. So while the PETM was marked by extinctions plus creations, what will happen during the coming abrupt changes? Are today's living things as able to adapt to warmer conditions?

At the very least, there is likely to be more migration of plants and animals than there has been already. But there's also the fact that much of the living space that animals and plants would have moved to has been transformed for human use. There could be a lot of dead ends on the migratory paths. This time, the pulse of extinction might happen without the pulse of new life.

We are even deeper into the Pyrenees now, on our last day of tramping the mountains. We've been climbing for more than an hour along the treacherous banks of Les Compes gully, a tributary of the Esplugafreda ravine. Wild lavender, oregano and thyme scent the torrid air, crushed by our steps. It's 38 degrees Celsius, midday and cloudless. Some of us are near heat exhaustion.

Fifty-five million years ago this was a coastal plain, probably partly arid. The internal evidence of the site suggests it had long, dry summers and huge cyclones and storms, formed while carbon concentrations in the atmosphere were rising. Sediments were laid down far more quickly than at other parts of the PETM, meaning that the energy of frequent storms and floods came into play, says Birger Schmitz, a geologist at the University of Lund, Sweden, who has been working at this site for years.

Huber's cyclone theory takes on a new significance for me.

Again the palaeontologists set to, hacking off samples to take home. They wrap them in wads of toilet paper and sheets of the *El Mundo* newspaper, like mummies, to dry them out and keep them safe until they can analyse them at their laboratories.

Off in the distance, climbing steadily in his hot plaid shirt, is a man I had assumed all along was another scientist. Last night I discovered he is Ron Waszczak, a senior staff stratigrapher with the Houston-based oil and gas firm ConocoPhillips. His job, he has told me, is to find new oil and gas reserves for his employer. He's here because of the tantalising stories Brinkhuis and Sluijs published in *Nature* about the Arctic expedition and the fact that so many fast-growing plants lived there fifty-five million years ago. To him, they weren't stories about the planet's potential for catastrophic change. They were stories about where to look for source rock for the next fossil fuel reserves.

CHAPTER 8

READING THE VITAL SIGN THAT IS CHINA

Haikou City: Slouching towards apoptosis?

As goes the global ocean, so goes life on the planet. This is beyond dispute. But here's an intriguing possibility. What if the rest of the equation reads this way: As goes *China*, so goes the global ocean?

If that's true—and it's shaping up to be—then life on the planet will hang on the economic and energy policies China chooses and helps promote to other fast-growing nations such as Brazil, India and Russia over the next two decades.

Despite its enormous importance, though, what China will do is a mystery. The People's Republic has policy plans for economic growth, population growth, fishing, aquaculture and control of carbon dioxide emissions that point in two ways at once: both towards a healthy future for the world and away from it to a very sick one. Either is possible. No one—not even the Chinese, and certainly not Westerners—knows which way it will go. China is the planet's great carbon enigma. That means it's important, when reading the sea, not to underestimate the power of this ancient and sophisticated people.

The idea that the planet's future might come down to China's choices is hard for people in the West to fathom. Westerners are used to thinking of China as a backwater, a view that the lavish summer Olympics in Beijing in 2008 was aimed at undermining. As well, China has had little to do with the centuries of industrial activity that have pushed up levels of carbon dioxide in the atmosphere and changed the ocean's chemistry. China's cumulative effect on the build-up of carbon dioxide has been minimal compared to Europe's or America's.

However, China has vaulted upon the world economic stage with ferocity—and therefore squarely into the international dramas of fossil fuels and carbon dioxide emissions—at a time when every molecule of carbon dioxide matters. This is the moment of truth for how humanity will cope with carbon pollution in the atmosphere and ocean. And China's economy is growing faster than that of any other country—by a huge margin. Its population, at 1.3 billion and already the largest in the world, is leaping ahead by about thirteen million a year, even with its one-child policy. It emits more greenhouse gases into the atmosphere than any other country and is also by far the planet's biggest player in the fishery and aquaculture, both of which affect the ocean's ability to keep itself healthy.

Consider the numbers: China has become the biggest emitter of greenhouse gases in the world, surpassing the United States of America in 2006, according to the Netherlands Environmental Assessment Agency. This has happened far more quickly than the international community expected. And China's emissions are continuing to grow, mostly from burning coal, the fuel that gives off more greenhouse gas than any other.

This is the result of China's extraordinary, sustained economic growth. From 1991 to 2005, China's rate of growth was an average of 10.2 per cent a year. The report *One Lifeboat: China and the World's Environment and Development* by Arthur Hanson and Claude Martin of the International Institute for Sustainable Development (IISD), says that China's economy is expected to continue to grow by at least 8 per cent a year into the future.

That would give China the third largest economy in the world by about 2015. Even Japan's economy during its phase of phenomenal growth increased at an average yearly rate of just 3.85 per cent from 1971 to 1991.

In 2007 alone China's gross domestic product grew a stunning 11.7 per cent, according to a report by Worldwatch Institute. That is a third of the increase in gross world product in that year. In all, notwithstanding recent embarrassing recalls of toxic consumer goods, the Chinese gross domestic product grew nearly six times as much as that of the US in 2007.

This growth has come from China's successful bid to become the world's factory. Quoting the newsmagazine *The Economist*, the IISD report says that China makes nearly a third of the world's television sets, half the world's cameras, seven in ten photocopiers and nearly a third of the furniture.

That's not all: 'China is now the largest consumer and producer in the world of many different commodities,' the report says. 'It is the second largest consumer of primary energy after the US, and the top global producer of coal, steel, cement and 10 different kinds of non-ferrous metals . . . In recent years, due to its robust growth, China has replaced the United States as the dominant market and price setter for copper, iron ore, aluminium, platinum . . .'

This trend has become so pronounced so rapidly—and so unexpectedly—that China's economic might and multibillion-dollar trade surplus with the US have become political fodder in America. And almost every bit of this torrid economic growth depends on the use of fossil fuels, and therefore on climate- and ocean-altering greenhouse gases.

Against that backdrop, it's easy to think of China as a nation whose policies support economic growth at all costs. But will China, coming of economic age now when the perils of carbon are so apparent, do what other developed countries have done and heedlessly push the world closer to catastrophe?

To try to get some understanding of even a little of China's strategy, I decide to attend an immersion course on the state of the Asian seas as a delegate at a high-level international marine meeting in Haikou City, Hainan Province, an island in the South China Sea.

It's a ground-breaking meeting of sorts. The Second East Asian Seas Congress is aimed at encouraging countries that border (or nearly border) the East Asian Seas—including China, Vietnam, Thailand, the Philippines, Japan, the Koreas, Indonesia, East Timor, Laos and Cambodia—to take a sharp look at how they are managing the health of the coasts and ocean around them, and to try to coordinate policies. This is where science meets the lawmakers.

The Congress's driving premise is that the East Asian Sea, one of the richest and most diverse of the world's ocean ecosystems, is a communal resource in a lot of trouble, and the people who depend on it must put aside historic differences in order to preserve its ability to provide food for them all. It's a simple enough concept, but cooperation among countries over marine bounty has rarely been achieved. (A classic example of failure is the European Union's current intractable mishmash of fishery policy.) The East Asian Sea, though, is one of the most highly degraded regional marine systems in the world, and it is called on to help support roughly two billion people who live near it— fully a third of the planet's human population.

Things are reaching a critical level. Nearly 90 per cent of the region's coral reefs are threatened and half are already in dreadful shape. Seventy per cent of the region's mangroves—a critical nursery for both land and sea creatures—have vanished in the past several decades, mainly cut down for short-term shrimp farms whose products are shipped to the West for cut-price sale. It's estimated that at this rate the mangroves throughout East Asia will have vanished by 2030. They represent a third of the world's mangroves. With the loss of both coral reefs and mangroves, the habitat for the most vulnerable marine life—including the hatchlings and embryos that grow to become fish—is also gone.

Rivers and coastal waters in this region are heavily polluted, mainly because so many humans live close to water and use it as a dump for chemicals, excessive fertilizers, sewage, and other substances they don't want. Some rivers have become lifeless; dead zones are forming off the coasts.

The Asian fishery is in trouble, too, just as it is everywhere else. A speaker from the World Bank explained that it takes more than three times the effort to catch a fish in the Philippines today than it did at the beginning of the 1990s, a pattern repeated throughout the region.

Chinese waters are so fished out that the government put a moratorium on summer fishing throughout its waters in 1998 and is trying to buy back fishing vessels. Other studies show that the fish caught in the East Asian Sea are lower and lower down the food chain. But the numbers on how many fish China has been catching over the years are suspect, so the actual catch trends there are not clear. In fact, inflated statistics about China's fish catch may have deluded the international community for years into thinking the global fishery was healthier than it actually was.

As for aquaculture, it is both the gold mine and the tragedy of Asia. As the fishery has declined, and as demand for fish has grown, aquaculture has taken off. In 1970 about 4 per cent of the fish and seafood humans ate came from farms; by 2004 it was a third. Aquaculture is growing faster than all other types of animal farming across the world. More than 80 per cent of that farmed seafood comes from Asia. And more than half the world's farmed fish and seafood comes from China alone. China has said it wants that percentage to grow.

However, farmed water animals need healthy places to live. So far, apart from a few vaunted experiments, aquaculture has created profoundly unhealthy places for animals to live, degrading water and land so that it cannot be used for other plants and animals. For example, not only have the life-giving (cyclone- and tsunami-breaking) mangroves vanished from the Asian coasts in favour of shrimp farms, but those farms have also pumped untreated shrimp waste back into the coastal waters. As Professor Mohamed Shariff, an aquaculture expert from Putra University in Malaysia, told the conference, sometimes the shrimp pollution—which he likened to espresso-coloured sludge—can spread as much as 3 kilometres off shore. Filled with phosphorus and nitrogen, it feeds toxic species of phytoplankton, which then gather in blobs and poison shrimp and fish. To keep their harvest alive, farmers then invest in antibiotics if they can afford them; these remain in the flesh of the animals and in their surroundings.

Eventually the shrimp ponds can no longer produce. It's the marine equivalent of slash-and-burn agriculture. Not only that, but the vast majority of farmed shrimp in China are *Penaeus vannamei*, imported in 1996 from Latin America without much research. These shrimp need less protein to grow fat than other shrimp and can live in both salt and fresh water, but they are vulnerable to Asian viruses as well as those from their home waters.

It strikes me, sitting in the opulent Haikou City People's Conference Centre, that this type of aquaculture seems like the case study of an enterprise fated to fail. Who thought this would work? Yet it's clear to many scientists and fisheries experts around the world that fish farming is the only way to ensure the world's population will have enough animal protein—the wild fishery will not withstand the level of catch that has been going on for the past decades. The trick will be to make sure the farming is done in an environmentally healthy, sustainable way.

There are far better models for aquaculture that could be implemented here, the world's fish-farming epicentre. One is Phil

Hart's enterprise. Hart, a former police sergeant, whom I met in Whyalla, South Australia, was one of the founders of a company that in 1998 became the first in the world to farm kingfish, a firm white-fleshed native of Australia that is superb for sashimi. He once took me around to the fish cages in Fitzgerald Bay in the northern part of the Spencer Gulf to show me the operation. These tide-drawn emerald waters, which face south to the South Australia Basin and into the Indian Ocean, are not pristine. But there's no agriculture and few humans live nearby. There's no chemical or organic waste being poured into the fish's living space.

Hart's business—which had just been sold to Clean Sea Group, one of the largest industrial fishery and aquaculture groups in Australia—was a fish-farm pioneer in South Australia.

He groaned slightly as he told me about the hoops he and his partners had to jump through to set up, but he's proud of how tough the standards were and how tightly the state of South Australia regulated the industry. It's the best example I've seen of science informing policy on a marine issue.

The fish Hart's company grows have to live naturally in that particular part of Fitzgerald Bay. They can't bring in foreign fish the way shrimp and salmon farmers all over the world have imported brood stock from strange waters. Experience has shown that fish tend to get sick if they aren't in their natural habitat. Cages have to be far enough apart and have few enough inhabit-ants that the sea-grass beds underneath remain undisturbed. The Asian practice of clearing the natural habitat is forbidden. As a result of the healthy environment, Hart's business has only had to use antibiotics on the fish twice in nearly a decade of farming.

Reporting to the government is intensive and ongoing. The company has to take samples of plants and animals on the sea beds surrounding and underneath the operation. They need a plan to prevent farmed animals from escaping into the open sea, and to make sure dolphins, sea birds and sharks aren't getting caught in the nets. They have to prove they aren't feeding the fish too much and fouling the bay.

Hart told me environmental inspectors come around with clipboards to verify results and then hold the fish farmers to what they say they're doing.

Ian Nightingale is the government official who administers the state's aquaculture legislation. When I left Whyalla and went to Adelaide to see him, he told me that his division did a great deal of scientific research on Fitzgerald Bay before it would allow Hart's farm to be built. Scientists produced conservative figures for how many farmed fish the bay could carry and Nightingale has not let them be exceeded. The farm also could not interfere with the movements of endangered sea lions in the bay.

In addition, the aquaculture legislation provides for both a licence and a lease for any fish farm, and each works as a check and balance on the other. It gives the government two ways to shut down an operation that doesn't meet its requirements. The state's independent environmental protection agency can also pull the plug if it doesn't like the results of environmental reports from the farms.

Nightingale knows that some fish farmers approach the business as a gold rush, but that's not what South Australia decided to do. He said that the state wanted fish farming to be a viable industry for the long term to replace some of the small land-farming operations that had vanished.

The day I was there, Nightingale was preparing for a visit from fish-farming officials from Tanzania. Officials from China had already come by to look, in addition to those from Japan, Indonesia and Vietnam.

Back in Haikou, the behavioural calcification that prevents the efficacy of this sort of sharing hits like a brick. Clearly a great deal of thought has gone into this conference. It's thick with policymakers, politicians, nongovernmental organisations and scientists. Yet, the litany of marine concerns discussed at the conference—dropping fish catches, local water pollution, off-shore dead zones, destructive aquaculture practices, lack of consensus over who gets what riches of the sea—are the traditional ones and reflect an ancient human understanding of the ocean, seen largely from the shore or from the surface. The ocean's depths, that 99 per cent of the planet's living space, its role in the world's life-giving chemistry and how humans are changing that, are not on the agenda. The world's policymakers have not yet grasped the urgency of these issues.

Global climate change comes up from time to time, but mainly as a separate problem that will raise the sea level and take away precious human living space and livelihoods and steal financial assets from those close to the shore.

Of thirty-nine workshops and seminars, 285 papers and posters, a ministerial forum and a youth event, the idea that carbon dioxide emissions are chemically affecting the ocean comes up just once, in a half-hour session by Michael Depledge and Michael Kendall, both based at Plymouth Marine Laboratory in England.

They are fluent, even passionate, in describing the fallout from the coming acidification of the ocean. Depledge argues for 'climate change' to be renamed 'ocean change' and warns of potential bursts of carbon that could create an alternate and less hospitable system: the changing Indian monsoon that could release a burp of methane, the melting permafrost that could do the same thing.

Kendall gives an elegant talk on the consequences of acidic seas. He raises the spectre of a shift in the whole marine food web.

'All these changes have happened before, but never, ever as rapidly,' he says. 'These are the fastest broad-scale changes the marine system has ever experienced.'

He is almost pleading at the end, telling the small break-out seminar that climate changes are already running ahead of projections. In the UK the scenario predicted for 2020 came to pass in 2006.

'We can't just sit on our hands and wait,' Kendall says.

It seems plain to me that all the problems people are talking about and trying to find solutions for here in Haikou City will be compounded by the chemical changes now happening in the ocean.

The day after the conference, officials from the East Asian Sea countries are hammering out a formal statement agreeing to meet in another three years with some more ideas on all these issues. Three years. The entrenched nature of humanity's ancient, parasitic relationship with the sea is hard to change.

With Mark Wunsch, a marine biologist from the Phuket Aquarium in Thailand, I hire a car to drive 300 kilometres down a perfect, wide highway to Sanya, a resort town on the southern tip of Hainan Island, jutting into the South China Sea. Sanya is home to a rather famous beach, a big tourist draw for China's growing, holidaying middle class. Much of the tourist fare is fish-related, or made from shells, including the inflated and dried blowfish sporting painted faces and small straw hats.

We see food vendors offering to grill shrimp. The shrimp are threaded, live and still wriggling, on bamboo skewers. Wunsch points up the road to a shrimp farm he's noticed on the way in. It's probably where these animals came from. I can only think of espresso sludge.

We are headed for Sanya's aquarium. Right inside its entrance is a shallow pool with an assortment of sea turtles swimming around. At the sight of us, one of the aquarium staff jumps to attention. Then he kneels at the side of the pool and drags one of the turtles out of the water, sits on it to keep it in place and stretches its neck out as far as it will go. He gestures to a plastic-covered photo of a smiling Chinese woman perched on top of this turtle or another, indicating that we too could have our picture taken for a price.

He tilts the turtle's mouth up, posing it for us.

We walk away. All species of sea turtles are endangered, many critically, despite the efforts of the world community to protect them from trade and aberrant exploitation like this. Their ancestors have been on the planet for more than 100 million years, surviving even the extinction of the dinosaurs. I remember the endangered green turtle I watched swimming on the vast expanse of the Great Barrier Reef, its movements unhurried, poetic.

Inside the aquarium building are the fish tanks. A few have sprigs of plastic aquarium plants in them, standing out against the swimming-pool tiles that line the backs of the tanks.

Wunsch is particularly interested in these displays so he can compare them to those at the Phuket Aquarium. The fish are hard to see: poorly labelled, or not labelled at all. It's not clear which ecosystems they come from; they seem to be just random fish. While some look healthy, others clearly have skin problems, a sure sign of disease. A fish in one of the tanks is swimming on its side near the surface.

In one tank, all of the dozens of inhabitants are gathered at the surface, gasping as if for air. Wunsch mentions that there is probably something wrong with the water's chemistry. He figures they will all be dead by morning. You can't mess with those biological limits.

A woman who works at the aquarium ushers us bossily out of the building and on to the next big attraction: the crocodiles. There are at least thirty sleepy-looking crocs in and around a concrete pond filled with soupy green water. The smell is enough to make me gag.

The pond is surrounded by an elaborate platform, complete with what looks like a disc jockey's set-up. The turtle wrangler appears again, this time with a baby croc whose jaw is taped shut so we can pose with it for pictures. I look away, wondering why a stringy brown chicken is on the platform, pecking away at the remains of a watermelon rind in a Styrofoam container.

Then the wrangler abandons the baby croc, swoops down and picks up the hen. It squawks vociferously. He makes as if to toss it to the crocodiles with one hand, rubbing his other thumb and two fingers together in the universal symbol for money. We refuse the live sacrifice and escape further along the croc pond, away from the platform.

Moments later a group of dozens of exuberant tourists comes through. Almost at once music starts up at the console, piped through impressive speakers. A guard comes over and shoos us away. If we don't pay, we don't get to take part in the fun. As we walk away, a drum rolls. I look back to see the crocs, which had been sunning themselves on the concrete, slide deftly into the water. They know what's coming.

On the long drive back to Haikou City, I have plenty of time for reflection. This was not an experience specific to China. Other countries have dreadful aquaria as well. In fact, what I saw in Sanya is not that different from the awful little zoo I visited in Kuranda, Queensland, in northern Australia. There, they have a staff of koala bears that tourists can cuddle and pose with, for a price. True, the human staff make a point of explaining that the koalas can only pose for 30 minutes a day, and only for three days in a row before having a day off. It's a better deal than Sanya's sea turtles and the crocodiles get, but it amounts to the same thing.

In microcosm, this is the way humans have traditionally related to animals, to nature. We have seen them in terms of what they can do for us, without regard to the damage we do to them. We haven't understood the whole picture, just little, select slices of it. We haven't known the dangers we run. And once we become aware of what damage we're doing to the whole system? Will that affect government policy, and individual action? Or will we just keep doing what we're doing and watch the system slouch toward apoptosis?

China does provide some clues. While it is clear that China is very far from a paragon on environmental fronts—including marine—and that it may not yet have figured out the future effects of ocean chemistry change, some of its recent policies have posited it as an international leader in green development. In a sense, because it is starting from a relatively low level of development, China has a free hand to be truly innovative.

Unbound by guilt over global climate change because it played such a small historic role in it, the Chinese central government appears to see clearly what the science is saying. It also grasps that the key to the continued growth it seeks is greater efficiency in the use of expensive natural resources. Waste is a barrier to growth. This is about survival in a rapidly changing world.

China can already track some effects of climate change on its own lands and coasts. By the central government's calculations, the average temperature in China has already risen more than the global average. For example, the country had twenty consecutive warmer-than-average winters from 1986 to 2005. Climate change is already causing droughts and floods in China; glaciers are in retreat all over the country; water quality is appalling; and the sea level is rising slightly more on average than in other parts of the world.

The result is that the Chinese central government has come out with muscular policies on both energy and climate change in recent months, putting the policies of many developed countries to shame. Embedded in the publicity around them is this fascinating paragraph, likely approved by the central government: 'In China, environmental protection and the conservation of energy and other resources are of paramount importance. It indicates how civilized a country really is.' (*China Daily*, 14 December 2007)

Given the disbelieving public statements on climate change, even in recent years, from political leaders in the United States, Australia and Canada among others, this is an astonishing position for a major world power to take. It is almost a rebuke.

So it seems China is staking its national pride on its green policies. And perhaps more: it appears to be keenly aware of its international responsibilities, of the fact that the fate of many other creatures depends on what it chooses to do. But it's impossible to know for sure how committed China is to these policies. The leaders could be posturing and, certainly, these are difficult policies to enforce. But China has already made astonishing progress in reducing the amount of energy needed to grow its economy. So while its economy has grown in recent years by about 10 per cent a year, its energy use has grown by the comparatively small 5.6 per cent a year. China has also gone far further than the North American recycling system, instead adapting the policies of Germany and Japan to form a 'circular economy', as the IISD report says. That means one industry's waste becomes another's raw material.

As well, China considers its controversial population policy part of a successful green plan. The one-child policy has kept China's population to about 1.3 billion today, rather than the 1.5 billion it would have been without the policy. That means the Chinese are using fewer of the earth's resources today than they might have been—the ultimate green policy.

China says it plans to go much further down the green road. Its list of climate change policies reads like the manifesto of an environmental nongovernmental organisation from the West. Its plans include integrating climate change policies with national social and economic policies—an intention frequently vowed by Western powers even as they fail to implement it—focusing on both preventing climate change and adapting to what's coming, using science and technology to find new ways of cutting down emissions and investing heavily in renewable energies such as wind and solar.

Among China's short-term goals is to reduce energy use by a fifth for every unit of gross domestic product by 2010, a bold move and one that other countries could learn from.

What does it mean for the global ocean? It's a mixed signal, but it's encouraging that it's not all negative.

China has forward-looking energy policies on the one hand, but a determination to grow quickly on the other. Half the buildings constructed in the world from now to 2015 are projected to be in China. They will use mainly coal for both construction and maintenance, releasing more carbon into the atmosphere and the ocean. Add this to industrial and manufacturing coal use and you have a lot of carbon dioxide emission. Still, China's plans for the reduction of energy use mean that less will be burned than might have been otherwise.

China is clearly a key player, but it's not the only country that will tell the tale of the sea. There is India, with its massive population and fast-paced growth, Brazil and Russia and, of course, the US with its incoherent policies for cutting carbon dioxide concentrations.

This is a lot of uncertainty given that we don't know how close we are to a tipping point in either atmospheric or ocean chemistry. Do we have years, decades, centuries, millennia? What is clear, though, as Kendall said, is that the global climate and ocean system is changing much more quickly than scientists have predicted, and those predictions have mainly ignored the particular stresses on the sea.

It seems to me that the key to understanding the impact of these changes on human life is not to look at the richest of us—who may be able to buy our way out of starvation or global panic—but, rather, at those who are already desperately poor, tied to a resource that's giving out. I decide to go and speak with some of the people who live on the Tanzanian island of Zanzibar.

CHAPTER 9

READING THE VITAL SIGNS: ADAPTABILITY

Zanzibar: Where the secrets of the sea converge

Here on the sand-swept archipelago of Zanzibar, the moon tugs at the ocean as it has for time immemorial, bringing two high tides and two low tides each day. And just as the moon pulls inexorably at the sea, so it pulls at the people who live on these islands. Many Zanzibari live by a lunar calendar, in deference to the rhythms of sea as well as to their Islamic faith. To them, life passes in time marked by the tides and the moon rather than where the sun is in the sky, a time-keeping method that Stone Age humanoids are thought to have developed. The critical switches between months depend on moonsets, lunations and lunar crescents. Seasons are governed by the monsoons.

It is a primordial rhythm. Even the sea creatures live by it, spawning and migrating according to signals they get from the moon, in turn triggering the Zanzibari fishermen to launch their wind-powered fishing boats into the Indian Ocean and lay their rudimentary nets. On the surface it seems as though over the millennia little has changed here on this Tanzanian archipelago a few kilometres off the coast of Africa, but deep down global changes have already affected the lives these Zanzibari are leading.

This is where all the secrets of the changing sea converge. Here, in one of the poorest countries on earth, is the place where scientific theory, climate models, acid tests, plankton research, massive swathes of oxygen-starved water, crumbling coral reefs and the pillaged fishery are already made manifest in the precarious body weight of the Zanzibari and their children. Zanzibar is a hint of how the changing vital signs of the sea will force humans to adapt. It is a sentinel archipelago: the people here on these moon-kissed islands are on the front lines. And they have few reserves—either bodily or financial—to do battle. And this is in the relatively early days of ocean stress. It's before the acidification of the sea increases, which could have catastrophic effects on Zanzibar's remaining coral reefs and the fish that depend on them. It is before the sea-level rise that could devastate villages and drown more corals. It is before changes to the temperature of the sea surface bleach more of the corals and push the fish towards the cooler water near the South Pole, and maybe alter the currents and monsoons that govern life on these islands.

Narriman Jiddawi is one of the few Zanzibari to understand the juggernaut that is on its way and to try to construct a defence against it.

A fisheries biologist and senior research fellow at Tanzania's Institute of Marine Sciences on Zanzibar's main island—called either Zanzibar Island or Unguja—she was recently named a fellow at the prestigious US-based Pew Institute for Ocean Science for her pioneering work in marine conservation.

Right now she is barefoot in a rental van with its pink linoleum floor in the sick-making heat of midday, swathed head to ankle in traditional Muslim dress, zooming over potholed roads toward the Zanzibari villages of Fumba and Bweleo to show me two of her prized ocean projects. As always she is carrying on several vehement conversations at once: with me, with two graduate students and with a government fisheries fellow who's come along for the ride.

Suddenly she belts out an order in Kiswahili. The van screeches to a halt. It's early February, by the Julian calendar, and the mangoes will never be better than right now. Some villagers have collected the fallen and are selling them by the side of the road.

Out Jiddawi gets, still barefoot, and starts a noisy, imperious negotiation, searching for the biggest, the juiciest, the most perfect mangoes. Triumphant, she returns to the van. She has scored six melon-sized mangoes for the equivalent of about 50 cents, and a 20-litre bucket of small mangoes for the same amount.

They were charging too little, she tells me, as we take off again. She shakes her head—they don't know what things are worth. She paid them double.

Jiddawi cannot bear the inequities that fall to people, especially those who are poor, African, Muslim and female. Her professional life is driven by the urge to right these wrongs, and her international reputation is based on the fact that she is capable of dreaming up practical solutions that will help. She is an extraordinarily tenacious woman.

Yesterday at her office in ancient Stone Town, the main city in Zanzibar, she told me that her projects in Bweleo and Fumba fall into the category of applied biology, verging on sociology. Fishing makes up about 10 per cent of the gross domestic product of Zanzibar; roughly a quarter of the islanders fish for a living. Almost all of it is artisanal, happening within about 20 metres of shore in boats with no motors. As much as 70 per cent of the animal protein that Tanzanians—including the Zanzibari—consume comes from fish. Fishing defines the island and its culture.

However, women are not allowed to fish. If a woman even happens to touch a fishing net, the net is considered cursed. That means that if a husband has a bad fishing day or week or month, the wife can't jump in a boat and try her own luck. She is shut out of the island's main economy and its main mechanism for getting food for her own table.

The coral reefs that fringe the island and provide living space for most of the fish are being systematically destroyed here, as in so many other places. Fishermen use dynamite or poison to catch their fish; others kill the coral and dig up their bony structures to make lime for Zanzibar's building industry, while higher temperatures from global climate change bleach the coral animals and kill them.

At the same time, fish are becoming so much rarer elsewhere in the ocean that poachers have begun targeting the waters surrounding Zanzibar. If that wasn't enough stress on the local ecosystem, the government—eager to alleviate the poverty that gives Tanzania the rank of 159th out of 177 countries on the United Nations' wellbeing index—opted several years ago to sell deep-sea fishery licences to foreigners who use the infamous industrial fishing methods of trawling and long lines. In the prophetic analysis of Boris Worm and Ransom Myers, this means that the fish numbers are poised to drop catastrophically in the next couple of years.

Together these trends mean that there are fewer places for fish and their young to live—leading to fewer fish, as well as far more pressure to catch those that remain.

On Zanzibar the fallout is that the men are catching fewer fish. And the old men say that the fish they do catch are also smaller. This coincides with a dramatic rise in the human population of Zanzibar, up from about 300,000 in the 1970s to around one million now. Additionally, over the past decade or so about 100,000 tourists a year flock to Zanzibar's snow-white beaches. Most of them like to eat fish—and not the little fish close to the bottom of the marine food web, but the increasingly rare fish at the top, such as marlin and tuna.

All these factors bring Jiddawi bumping over the axle-breaking roads on her way to Bweleo and Fumba. While women are banned from fishing, over the ages they have been allowed to collect seaweed and shellfish such as oysters and clams from the tidal zones. But as their families have become hungrier and the sea more degraded, the women, in their turn, have begun collecting too many shellfish. So a couple of years ago Jiddawi, with help from Israeli and American scientists, set up some experimental farms in tidal pools where the women can rear oysters, clams and other shellfish, and either eat them or sell them to tourists. This was an add-on to the low-tech seaweed farms some of the women were already running.

Hauke Kite-Powell, an aquaculture specialist at Woods Hole Oceanographic Institution in the US who was involved in setting up the farms, has been telling me about them. They started about 1989, when some Zanzibari women began farming seaweed for the international pharmaceutical industry, one of the few obvious inroads the globalised economy has made into this island. The women string lines between stakes in the tidal pools near their villages, tie bits of seaweed to them, let them grow and then harvest, dry and sell them to the pharmaceutical companies who derive the natural emulsifier carrageenan from the seaweed.

At the beginning, says Kite-Powell, the women made money. Then the practice of farming seaweed spread, the supply rose and the prices went down drastically. Some of the women at Bweleo still have tiny seaweed farms, but Jiddawi could see the proverbial writing on the wall and figured that shellfish farms would help increase the women's income—or, at least, their protein levels.

By the time we get to Bweleo it's a low tide, at the end of a spring tide. In the language of Zanzibar, that means it's the new moon. Four of the several dozen women involved in the projects are waiting for us, barefoot and dressed in colourful hijab: Amina Khamis, Fatma Ramadhan, Subira Vuai and Mwatum Juma.

They are some of the original seaweed farmers who have now added shellfish to their repertoire.

They lead us to the seemingly endless beach. Pure white sand is framed by a sky so blue that most Westerners could not even imagine the colour. A few dhows float in the distance. A man tinkers with his nets on the beach and some boys are playing with handmade sailboats. It is violently hot under the midday sun.

This is the way most humans picture the ocean, as a relatively simple, flat entity that fills in the spaces between land. It is an ancient, iconic image. I think of those first humans to settle at the sea 150,000 years ago on the South African cape. This must be similar to what they saw. The ocean looks so immutable, so dull— so unimportant.

I can taste salt in the air as I walk with the women toward the sea. The sand sucks me down, footstep by footstep. The sound of the wind fills my ears, to the exclusion of all else. Around me are expansive beds of sea grasses, the most extensive I've ever seen. I think about Heike Lotze and the Wadden Sea, where the locals destroyed all the sea grasses in the Middle Ages. One of the women bends down from the waist, her skirt dragging in the water, head carefully draped, to show me a sea cucumber and a sea urchin. The others gather around as Jiddawi translates from Kiswahili into English for me, patiently drawing pictures of the creatures in my notebook and writing the Latin names beside.

The women fan out along the beach, each heading towards her own farm. Each farm is a circle of sticks perhaps a couple of metres across. Here an oyster is attached to the formation, there a mussel. The shellfish feed on plankton, so the tides bring them food. The women just give them a place to grow, tend them and harvest them when they're ready. There's little, if any, interference with the natural systems here.

This is not the large-scale, industrial farming of Scotland, China and North America that feeds big carnivorous fish with protein pellets made from little ground-up wild fish and krill, and that adds antibiotics and chemical colourings to the pellets, affecting the life below the fish pens. It's a different paradigm.

It also doesn't take much financial outlay from the women or their families. Jiddawi has helped the women collect seed stock for the shellfish by getting them access to a boat so they could go further out to sea to some tiny, less depleted islands. These farms are actually helping the environment by taking some pressure off the wild shellfish. Plus, they're bringing the women food.

These women are used to eating little. A study from 2001 showed that more than a third of Zanzibari children are underweight. A more recent look at infants nine to eighteen months old on the island of Pemba found that 81.4 per cent were either stunted, wasted or underweight. Nearly 84 per cent were anaemic.

The life expectancy across the nation of Tanzania is fifty-one years.

Jiddawi explains to me that during the spring tides, known here as *bamvua*, the moon pulls hard at the water, causing the highest and lowest tides twice each month for a week at the new moon and again at the full moon. This is when the men fish and, therefore, these families eat.

In between the *bamvua* are the neap tides, when the moon is weaker. That's one week after the new moon as well as one week after the full moon. There's not so much difference between the low and high tides then and the fishermen of Zanzibar are less likely to catch fish. Then, if they have money, they eat. If not, they go hungry.

So when the women of Bweleo started growing seaweed and then rearing shellfish, the men were happy, the women tell me, smiling and nodding. It took some of the pressure off, especially given that catches overall are down.

They are proud of what they've done here. One of the women tells me that she bought a cupboard for her kitchen from the money she made seaweed farming. The cupboard is one of her treasures. Most of all, though, the women are just grateful that they can feed their children.

To Kite-Powell this is clearly the way of the future, not just here in this poor community, but the world over. Fish farming is the only way to increase the global supply of seafood, he argues. And humanity has come relatively late to it, medieval carp ponds notwithstanding.

The sticking point is that the farming must not foul its own environment. We have to figure out how to do it right, so it can last.

'The question is not whether it's possible, but how to go about it,' he told me.

Zanzibari shellfish farmers are on the front lines of the effects of ocean change, but just maybe they are also pioneers in a new, low-tech world trend.

We passed a smoking structure on the way here and now one of Jiddawi's graduate students is giving me a chemistry lesson, the reverse of the one that Joanie Kleypas taught me about how the seas become more acidic.

This lesson also concerns the calcium carbonate that the coral animals use to build their bony skeletons. As the sea becomes more acidic from the carbon dioxide we are putting into the atmosphere, the shell-building calcium becomes less available. This is the most worrying of all the changes to the ocean because we don't know and can't predict how marine life will react to the new ocean chemistry.

Zanzibar Island is an ancient coral reef. Now dead, the reef became an island during the Pleistocene epoch when the sea level fell. The coral rag, or ancient dead coral, is mined as a key building material on the island. It has been mined for as long as anyone remembers and is one of the island's main industries.

Once mined it's put into an open kiln, laid down in layers separated by coconut logs, firewood and coconut husks, and set to burn for three or four days. At some point the coral skeleton bursts into a powder. When heated, the calcium carbonate of a coral skeleton creates calcium oxide—which we know as lime—and carbon dioxide gas.

Builders throughout Zanzibar mix the lime with sand and mud to make cement. They also use the lime for whitewash to paint the exteriors of the island's buildings. It's a key element of the picture-postcard cachet of Stone Town, which is named after the coral stone it's built on. For some of the builders, however, it's more convenient to make lime out of live coral from the sea than the dead stone under their feet. The practice is endemic and the living reefs are suffering, adding yet another pressure on the coral ecosystem so critical to the Zanzibari—and the world. The practice is also an excellent way of putting yet more carbon dioxide into the atmosphere.

By the time we get to Fumba, it is too hot to walk on the beach. There's not a cloud in the sky. Jiddawi takes me to see some of the women in the village. We pass an enormous pile of cockle shells, refuse from an old cash crop. The tiny house beside it has walls of shiny lime green instead of the usual whitewash—luxury.

Down at the edge of the beach five of the farming women are waiting for us, sitting in a circle on pieces of cement under a coconut thatch lean-to, covered head to foot in their light drapes of cloth. Jiddawi sits on a rusted barrel stuck in the sand.

I'm still not understanding how the moon—rather than this ever-present, scorching sun—governs their lives. Patiently, they explain that it's not just the moon. It's more complex than that.

The ocean also depends on the winds, they say. Right now, we are in the *kaskazi*, meaning the northeast monsoon season from December to March by the Julian calendar. Jiddawi sketches the archipelago and the eastern coast of Africa in my notebook in broad, black strokes, drawing in the directions of the winds. During *kaskazi*, the winds move from the north and blast toward the west side of the archipelago.

The other main season—running from June to August—is the *kusi*, or the southeast monsoon, which is when the winds and currents batter the island from the south and blow up against the east coast of Africa. These are stronger than the *kaskazi* winds.

The catch depends on the monsoon, as well as the lunar calendar and the tide.

This way of understanding the passing of time is bred in the bones of these women. Time is a rhythm. I hate to imagine how global climate and ocean change will affect these rhythms. Will the monsoons wither or grow? What will the fish do? In a hundred years, will the offspring of these women still count on the moon and the tides and the winds?

The women turn to Jiddawi. Yesterday nine boats were fishing off shore, dragging nets with small mesh. The women have been seeing this more often—another sign of big change. These are illegal fishermen using illegal gear designed to catch fish too young to have reproduced. This whole area—Jiddawi sweeps an arm in the direction of the sea—is a conservation area and shouldn't be fished by outsiders at all.

Back in Stone Town, the sun is mercifully setting. Small boys dressed in white leggings, long shirts and white caps run merrily through the warren of crumbling streets on their way to prayer with the older men. Their ankles are skinny under their flowing trousers. Mangoes are ripe here, too, and the boys toss juicy pits, stripped bare of flesh, into the streets. There are too many to eat, so some of them rot in the streets.

This ancient town is beautiful, redolent of all the historic trends of the sea: the brave quest for trade and spice routes, the dreams of conquerors and migrants, the hardships of slavery and the fight for emancipation. It is one of the oldest cities in the world and was recently named a world heritage site for its distinctive culture and iconic, whitewashed architecture. More than half these architectural jewels are set aside for the poorest of the poor, paid for by the state.

At night tourists congregate on the west side of Stone Town in the grassy garden on the beach. The beauty of the sea is preternatural; the dark of the night, absolute. Only the stars give off light, apart from the long row of open-fire barbecues lined up along the beach. Smoke hangs in the air.

Here is the day's catch, cut up and strung on skewers for pennies a stick: marlin, tuna, shark. These are all the fish rich in calories and globally depleted that the locals never eat, saved for those of us born in wealthier parts of the world. At this moment, the systems we humans have set up seem horribly unfair and intractable.

FINDING HOPE

Journey to the deeps, in the Dry Tortugas south of Florida

Hope skitters back and forth across time, lingering both in the past and in the future. Unlike despair, which burns up the present and obviates all else, hope is dependent on context. With hope, either you believe in patterns adduced from the past and extrapolated to the future or you abandon them, which is why hope is intrinsically absurd. You are compelled to use the gift of logic, and then rely instead on the irrational, the unexpected.

Why do we hope? This is still a mystery, one of a slender roster of conundrums that even poets have failed to reveal. We have plausible theories, for example, of how the universe came to be and how the genomic inner workings of a cell operate, how light and time and space function. But we have not parsed the structure of hope, which may be why we long for this remaining mystery to prevail, even as we fear losing faith with it.

Or so it seems to me, at least, as I prepare to board a tiny submersible vessel that is to take me to the bottom of the sea off the Florida Keys, the final research expedition for this book.

I'm out of hope, mired firmly in the desolate present.

I am an empiricist and the evidence about the advanced

illness of the global ocean and its enervated vital signs has seemed to build a terrifyingly strong case of incalculable disaster. It is as though the earth's cancer, whose primary site is the atmosphere, has metastasised to the ocean, making the disease far harder to treat. I've begun to think that the ocean is in palliative care and I a mute witness to its death rattle.

Why keep going, I was asking myself. *Why should another research trip make any difference?* But I had learned of this research from Mike Roman, my tutor on the ScanFish in the Gulf of Mexico, and had made arrangements many months earlier to take this dive 914.4 metres (3000 feet) to the bottom of the ocean. It was to be a journey to a part of the ocean never before seen by human eyes, to look for compounds from deep-sea animals that may someday—with ingenuity, patience and luck—cure cancer.

So this was not to be a trip to look at yet another element of the ocean that was going wrong. It was aimed at trying to understand, for a few hours, what it was like to be deep inside the ocean womb, where the human hand had not yet touched. It was the final test, the end point of my personal journey to conquer the paralysing fear of being under the surface of the water. It was to be a rite of passage.

Now it seems like a late dash to capture some more goods of the sea before we spoil them all. It is tinged with irony. Surely hope does not lie at the bottom of the sea.

Amy Wright, a marine scientist at Harbor Branch Oceanographic Institution in Florida, is my guide to the sea floor this June morning. Along with her colleagues Shirley Pomponi and John Reed, she operates the *Johnson-Sea-Link I* and *II*, two of only a couple of dozen craft in the world that go deep for ocean research. Together, Harbor Branch's twin vessels have logged more than 9000 trips to the deeps.

It's small comfort as I cast my glance on the *Johnson-Sea-Link II* that will carry me below. We only arrived on board late last night and I'm seeing the machine for the first time, just as I'm about to get in. The front part, where Wright and the submersible's pilot, Phil Santos, will sit, is a tough, 13 centimetre-thick acrylic sphere loaded with controls. These allow the pilot to drive the submersible once the ship has launched it into the open sea. (That's the difference, as I've been told, between a submersible and a submarine: the submersible is dependent on a ship.) And while some submersibles are tethered to the mother ship, ours is not. Once it hits the water it's an independent traveller, run off fourteen two-volt battery cells.

The controls also allow the pilot to manoeuvre a robotic claw, a scoop and a suction tube to capture whatever deep-sea animals the scientist wants and place them in containers to bring them to the surface. The back part of the submersible is where I'll be, along with Frank Lombardo, the craft's electronics technician, who is a dead ringer for the American actor George Clooney. It's made of aluminum and gets very cold in the deeps. I've been told to bring everything warm I own—that's five layers and a blanket.

It dawns on me that at this moment I'm past hope or despair: I'm caught tight in the grip of fear. Almost everyone else on board is pumped—apart from the nervous grad students who, like me, are slated for their inaugural dives during this week-long expedition—eager to get going, excited to be exploring this part of the ocean, at the treasures yet to be discovered there.

Pomponi strolls over and asks me how I'm doing. I tell her I'm scared. She is an eminent scientist and she brings a scholar's mind to this information, assembling her facts logically. To her, this is an issue of mathematical probability. Well, she says, we've only lost two people in more than 9000 dives, and that was a long time ago. Both died in the same back chamber you'll be in, she mentions.

I am silent.

She continues. 'The air in your chamber is recycled. A scrubber system removes the carbon dioxide you exhale and puts it into the ocean just outside the chamber. Then we add more oxygen to the air in the chamber to keep you alive. The others died because the submersible got caught and the scrubber stopped working. The carbon dioxide hit lethal levels. But,' she adds reassuringly, 'we've replaced the scrubber since. It's quite safe, quite safe.'

With that, I am at the base of the submersible's back entrance, climbing through the craft's hatch into the aluminum chamber. I have to lie down to fit. Lombardo comes up after me, clangs the hatch shut and lies down beside me. I have the sensation of being shut into the coffin space left when you put two bathtubs one on top of the other. I can sit up only if I hunch my back. We will be in here for a little more than three hours, most of that at around the crushing depth of 914.4 metres.

Lombardo explains about the carbon dioxide scrubber and points behind me to the scrubber's fan. That's supposed to hold the carbon dioxide at 0.4 per cent of the air inside this chamber, as long as I don't block it too much. I press my body away from it, acutely aware of the need to avoid interfering with its work.

I've done vast research on the composition of the atmosphere, on how the planet's life-support systems work, on the boundaries that limit life, the utter dependence humans have on the planet's complex biological systems, and nothing really brings it home like being here in this microcosmic aluminum chamber. The chemistry and physics of the global ocean are about to become unavoidably real.

There's a gauge that measures the oxygen content of the chamber's air; it needs to stay below about 21 per cent oxygen. Too much oxygen is as fatal as too little. As well as the gauges, which can fail, there's the more immediate test of how Lombardo and I are feeling. If we start to get dreadful headaches, we'll know that the proportion of gases is off.

Lombardo takes me through a lesson on the emergency gear. There's a back-up battery in case the submersible drops its main battery pack. Our chamber's atmosphere is separate from that of the front sphere, which means that if we have problems, the people in the front can still survive, or vice versa. There's a fire extinguisher. (I have failed to worry about the possibility of an oxygen-sucking fire in the chamber until this very moment.) And over there is scuba gear on the off chance we need to use its breathing apparatus or enter the water. Of course, scuba divers are not known to thrive below 54 metres and we are going to 915. Still, I figure, it's something.

Then it's time for a primer on what I would need to do to get the submersible to the surface from this back chamber, in case the other three people on board couldn't do it. I am terribly alert as Lombardo talks.

Then we are off, launched from the ship by a contraption that reminds me of a giant swing set. We descend at the rapid pace of 30 metres a minute into this mystery-filled third dimension of the ocean. Lombardo checks the seal on the hatch to make sure no water is pouring in (another risk I had failed to worry about until then, and it occurs to me that there must be many more) and settles down to read a paperback novel in the dim light.

To him, to Wright and Santos, to Pomponi and Reed, this is all in a day's work, the way flying is for airline crews. Each has been down hundreds of times. Lombardo stopped counting a couple of years ago when he got to 650 dives. The thrill for them is the quest to find new deep-sea animals that may produce unheard-of compounds that could help medicine.

Why deep-sea animals? The deep-sea sponges, sea fans and other creatures that they're in search of can't move. In scientific terms they're sessile, meaning they can't stroll over to a potential mate and tap him on the shoulder. They can't leap across a breach to capture a tasty bite of lunch or run to hide from a hungry enemy. Instead, they must communicate chemically. To do that, they have evolved a sophisticated chemical arsenal. These chemicals—unknown in the rest of nature and unimagined by humans—allow the stationary creatures of the abyss to fend off predators, attract prey and lure mates.

Wright is already an international superstar in the arena of finding drugs from the sea. It's a field that has been active since 1967, when the National Institutes of Health in the US began to sponsor research in it. In fact, Wright's chemical research has been a key in the development of the drug Yondelis (also known as ecteinascidin 743, ET-743 and etrabectedin). If it's approved, it will be the first drug found from a marine creature to be used on cancer patients.

As we descend today, Yondelis is in the third phase of trials in Europe for use as a drug of last resort for ovarian cancer. It's showing promise in treating metastasised cancers of the breast, colon and lung, as well as skin cancer. Wright is crossing her fingers that it will be approved for use in Europe soon.

In 1985 and 1986 she went collecting in the Florida Keys and found a little sea squirt—*Ecteinascidia turbinata*—in a marine mangrove forest. Her team ground it up and did a trial on its chemical compounds, only to find that it worked incredibly well against leukaemia in animals.

From there, Wright purified the compound. Some of the compound's chemical structure had already been worked out by her colleague Ken Rinehart in Illinois, but Wright pinpointed the final piece, a process very like solving a three-dimensional crossword puzzle. The drug itself is made from a synthetic version of the same compound, rather than from live sea squirts.

The fascinating thing about Yondelis is that it works on cancer cells in a new, different way from other cancer drugs. It binds with the minor groove of the cell's DNA and triggers apoptosis, making the cell kill itself. One of the characteristics of cancer cells in general is that they fail to self-destruct when they ought to, and keep reproducing to produce tumours. Triggering apoptosis in a cancer cell—so that the healthy cells can survive and flourish—is one of the dreams of modern cancer research.

The compound in Yondelis also appears to interfere with a membrane protein that protects the cancerous cell from absorbing toxic substances such as chemotherapy drugs.

In other words, Yondelis breaks down the cancer cell's dogged ability to stay alive, and this is why doctors have high hopes for it to be used as part of an anti-cancer cocktail.

Even more fascinating, Yondelis is the first new drug to be found in more than twenty years to treat the rare but deadly class of soft-tissue sarcomas.

I can hear Wright now, talking into a video that is being made of everything she's seeing. A monitor measuring about 13 centimetres by 13 centimetres is above my head, so I will be able to track what's she's seeing from her seat in the front bubble. I also have two tiny, thick portholes through which I can look out into the deeps. About two minutes into the dive, at about 60 metres, we lose sight of the sun's rays. It is, as the abyssal explorer Robert Ballard writes in his book *The Eternal Darkness: A Personal History of Deep-Sea Exploration*, 'much more oppressive than the blackest chamber inside any cavern on land'.

Suddenly, I think of Olaus Magnus and the map he made of the North Sea in 1539. For the first time I understand exactly why his ocean was thick with fearsome monsters. It's scary and alien down here. It is like facing the demons within.

As we descend, tiny luminescent organisms flicker and flash, the only points of light. We see marine snow, clumps of decomposing bodies—mainly plankton—from further up that fall to the seabed like snowflakes to be recycled as food and organic chemicals for other creatures. We are witnessing carbon being stored in the deep ocean, where it will stay for centuries or more, depending on where it falls. This is the day-to-day working of the complex chemistry of life on earth.

It's getting colder.

Santos announces that we're at 610 metres now. I'm shivering, wearing every jacket I've brought on board. Lombardo, reading his paperback, casually pulls up the hood of his top. The monitor says it's 6.9 degrees Celsius; up there at the surface it's more like 30 degrees Celsius. Just as light doesn't penetrate this far, neither does heat. And humans, only rarely. Mainly, those who come here are specialist scientists and naval crew.

All I can think about is the deadly weight of the water on top of me, and that the water's physical imperative is to get into this nice, empty space Lombardo and I are inhabiting. The mathematics work like this: at the surface of the ocean, you have the weight of one atmosphere of pressure on you, or about 4 kilograms per square centimetre. Our bodies are perfectly suited to that. For every 10 metres you go below the surface of the ocean, you have the pressure of another full atmosphere on you. That's an additional 4 kilograms per square centimetre. If you're a deep snorkeller, a free-diver or a scuba diver, you know the feeling of the water's pressure on your eardrums as you descend. Here at 610 metres below the surface— and dropping—the pressure is already the equivalent of more than 60 atmospheres, or 200 kilograms per square centimetre. Once we get to the bottom at 914 metres, it will be more than 90 atmospheres, or more than 300 kilograms per square centimetre.

This is by no means the deepest slice of the ocean floor. Like the land surface of the planet—except more extreme on all counts— the ocean's bottom has high peaks, medium-sized hills and low valleys. The very deepest part is the Mariana Trench in the Pacific Ocean, where it descends to nearly 11 kilometres. Only two humans have seen it, and only once, on 23 January 1960.

If our hull developed a leak or a crack even at our depth, the water would rush into the chamber, killing us instantly. This is one reason the acrylic front chamber and the aluminum back chamber are separate. If one gets damaged, the other could still remain intact and be able to get back up.

As Ballard explains, the animals that live this deep are adapted to the pressure because they are filled with water from the same depth.

'A diving craft, however, is a hollow chamber, rudely displacing the water around it,' he writes in *The Eternal Darkness*, a passage that is burned indelibly in my memory as I lie here in this frigid shell. 'That chamber must withstand the full brunt of deep-sea pressure . . . If seawater with that much pressure behind it ever finds a way to break inside, it explodes through the hole with laserlike intensity. A human body would be sliced in two by a sheet of invading water, or drilled clean through by a narrow (even a pinhole) stream, or crushed to a shapeless blob by a total implosion.'

The immense weight of ocean water has been one of the big barriers to deep-sea exploration. Not only does it make deep diving dangerous, but devising hulls that can withstand that pressure also makes it expensive. Humans have spent centuries trying to get past the first few metres in a range of diving bells, bathyspheres and other contraptions.

It was only in 1930 that William Beebe and Otis Barton became the first humans to descend to 434 metres under the surface of the ocean in a submersible. They stayed for mere moments. As Ballard recounts, Beebe said that looking down into the abyss was like seeing 'the black pit-mouth of hell itself'. Four years later the same pair reached 923 metres, remaining there for three minutes. That record for depth stayed intact for fourteen years.

Since then humans have figured out how to go deeper. This craft I'm on, the *Johnson-Sea-Link II*, can go to 914 metres. The more famous *Alvin*, a submersible run by the Woods Hole Oceanographic Institution in Massachusetts and owned by the

US Navy (Ballard used it to find the *Titanic*), can reach nearly 4570 metres and stay for up to ten hours at a time.

Rather too casually, I ask Lombardo what would happen if we sprang a leak.

'I would fix it,' he says calmly. He adds that he's not worried about 'catastrophic' leaks because he and all the other non-scientists who travel on the submersible also do the repairs and maintenance on it. They're highly motivated to make sure things work well.

Still, the feeling of vulnerability is a thing alive. We four representatives of our voracious, casually destructive species are here in the belly of the planet's fundamental life force, at the mercy of a system we are only beginning to understand. We are immersed. There's no way out except back up the way we came.

Then we hit bottom: 914.4 metres. It's now 5.9 degrees Celsius. The cold is viscous.

Santos turns on the xenon arc lights that illuminate the inky marine blackness for about 15 metres in front of us. We are at the bottom of a sheer-faced sinkhole in the Tortugas Valley, beyond the continental shelf south of Florida. The wall in front of us runs straight up for 119 metres, stark as an iceberg. The scientists are hoping that this kind of wall will be prime real estate for deep-sea sponges and sea fans, which is why we're here. Wright is on the lookout for specimens to take to the surface.

We are the first humans to see this, and perhaps the last. Lombardo has abandoned his novel. 'It's pretty cool,' he murmurs, peering out the porthole. 'Very few people have ever been this deep. Nobody has ever seen this before.'

I see hollows and crevices and animal bore-holes in the wall in front of us, and little shrimp poking their heads out of them. Wright says, with disgust in her voice, that the wall face looks as though it's made of Silly Putty. She was hoping for a hard rock surface because her sponges like to attach to that.

Life is everywhere. Over there, a field of tiny pink sea fans, an anemone, a pile of coral rubble; there, some eels, unidentified fish, a giant squid, crabs, a black lobster with eyes that glow eerily white, some ancient brachiopods whose ancestors first appeared more than three billion years ago. A small fish swims past my head as I peer out the porthole; it is no bigger than my fingernail, delicate pink. All around us is the marine snow, suspended as if in solution.

The hand of *Homo sapiens* is here but invisible. Even this deep, the fossil-fuel-based carbon dioxide that we have pumped into the atmosphere can be tracked chemically. At this depth, salinity patterns have already changed from the volume of glacier ice melting in the climate-change-induced heat of the air, and the temperature of this water has already risen slightly.

Reed—who has boxes of decades-old, carefully annotated geological papers on board for his dive-site research—has explained to me that humans only became aware of the topography of this part of the ocean in 1838, during the first hydrographic survey of this area. More than a century later, in 1954, a seismic survey running from Key West to Cuba discovered this sinkhole, an unusual ocean-floor formation. In the 1990s a nuclear submarine passed over the area with a side-scan sonar to catch a clearer outline of the sinkhole's shape. By the time we, the first people, are here for the first time, this unexplored, unexploited corner of the ocean is nonetheless already chemically altered by human activity elsewhere.

I think about a dinner I had a few months ago in England, with the brilliant scientist Carol Turley of Plymouth Marine Laboratory. She's known as the acid queen in the UK for her formidable work explaining the changing pH of the global ocean. She's a big thinker, a synthesiser, like Tim Flannery. I've come to think of her as the oracle of the deeps.

Some of her earlier work was on marine snow and she spent part of our dinner explaining the characteristics of the planet's deep ocean water to me. Like the rest of the planet's deep water, this batch the submersible is in right now is made up of water of different ages, created in all sorts of different places at different times. It is forever in motion, but different parts of it are moving in different directions. As we forage around down here, we are literally moving across the dimension of time, through past, present and future water. And there's another layer of time laid over the top of this. Some of the biological processes of this part of the ocean are local and immediate—like the plankton blooms at the surface, the day-to-day activity of fish and other marine creatures. Some are tied to the ocean's seasonal cycles, some to annual patterns and some to events that happen only once in several million years.

It's like being immersed in the Australian Aboriginal concept of Dreamtime—or anywhen—when time ceases being a straight line or even a cycle, and all time exists simultaneously. Previously I have only understood this idea intellectually. Now, I feel it. I live it. It is indescribably shattering.

People who go to extreme environments—astronauts and deep divers—often report odd experiences. It has something to do with being pushed past a limit. Some become emotional, focusing on intensely personal issues such as an unresolved relationship with a parent. Others turn to a religious faith. And yet others go on a surprising intellectual journey to the abstract. This is where I have gone, deep into the theories of time and dimension. And now the epiphany comes. My fear vanishes, as does my despair. I feel as though I have burst through this cramped space and out into the whole world.

I'm flooded with hope, with a sweet consciousness of the rich march of time, stretching from the deep past to the remote future, each moment containing all the others. It is impossible to think only in the self-indulgent, despairing, fearful present when surrounded by life across these four dimensions. All this time, through all these voyages, I've been trying to reason my way to hope, to convince myself that hope is justified, to build a case. It's been the question I asked all the scientists I met.

In fact, hope just is. You can't run through a checklist to get to it. Yes, it is absurd and irrational. But, like love, it is human. Like laughter, hope catches and spreads. It works logarithmically, like the changes now under way on our planet, like our growing understanding of them and like our powerful collective human ability to start coping with them.

That doesn't mean that hope is naïve. Shivering in my undersea womb, peering at these wondrous, ancient life forms, it occurs to me that we are in an era that holds out the potential of magnificent regeneration. We could, if enough of us wanted to, form a new relationship with our planet. We could become the gentle symbionts we were meant to be instead of the planetary parasites we have unwittingly become. Perhaps this is the system switch that will be in the offing. Instead of the ocean lurching further into an irrevocably altered state, maybe humans will irrevocably alter our relationship to it and understand that we must keep it healthy if we are to save ourselves.

The point, as Turley explained to me, is that biology—and that includes our species—is at work all the time. It is flexible, adaptable. It works in four dimensions all at once: breadth, width, depth and time. It can always surprise us, can always do the unexpected. This is the ocean's prophecy.

Wright has spotted her sponges. They are otherworldly. One is yellow. A second is enormous, shaped like a white glass tulip on a reddish stalk almost a metre high. The white tulip-shaped sponge has long silica fibres attaching it fiercely to the sandy bottom. Clear and long, these tenacious organisms are the original fibre-optic material.

Santos collects them carefully with the robotic implements and puts them in containers hooked to the front of the submersible, so we can take them to the lab on board the ship hovering so far above us.

This isn't as good a haul as Wright wanted, but it's new genetic material to work on. Maybe these animals will be the ones to contain a surprising new way to nudge cancer cells toward apoptosis.

Now it's time to wrap up. The batteries are getting low; we're at our limit. Up we go, back to the surface.

Three months after we finish our trip, the European Commission approves Yondelis for use throughout Europe against soft-tissue sarcomas that can't be cured by anything else.

A CALL FOR WISDOM

Truth lies in the tales we tell rather than in the scientific facts that give rise to them.

So, understanding the meaning of the changes to the global ocean requires more than knowing that human activity is pushing the ocean's chemistry and biology towards a state it has not been in for millions of years. It takes stepping outside the science and into the curious realm of human psychology, where the stories we weave around the facts are born.

It is possible, for example, to look at what's happening to the global ocean and conclude that it is insignificant, either because the science must be wrong or because humans simply can't have this much power over the planetary systems.

It is possible to look at the facts and decide that the ocean will right itself without our help, possibly through an outside force swooping in, whether divine, technological or otherwise super-human. This is one of humanity's most ancient and cherished stories and it runs through culture and time. Recent news accounts featuring the governor of Alabama praying for rain in the climate-change-parched croplands of his state are an example of this. A key belief underpinning this tale is that humans deserve salvation.

Or here's another view, the guilt-ridden one: we may as well carry on as we are because we deserve to be annihilated for being such idiots. Or there's the story that the changes to the global ocean are so serious that they will kill us no matter what we do, so we may as well dance the merry jig of death. This is the mentality that characterised the plague years in Europe during the fourteenth century: we're going to die anyway, so we may as well eat, drink and spend as if tomorrow will never come.

I'd like to suggest a different interpretation: ocean change is extremely serious and we have some power to halt or reverse it if we alter our actions rapidly, profoundly and en masse. This draws on the archetypal human story that we can face the demons of the deeps—or journey to the underworld or wrestle with the devil's temptations or plunge to the psychological abyss—and come back to tell the tale. We can triumph, lead and heal. This is Odysseus, Aeneas, Hercules, Sinbad. It is the human epic.

The story we tell matters because it alone determines the actions we take or fail to take. In other words, the final vital sign of the global ocean is how the agent of destruction—us—will react. Will we turn the destruction off? Will we nudge towards our own self-destruction so that the earth can survive? Will we continue to attack the organism of the earth, pushing it into a new system that will be unlikely to harbour us?

The problem of the atmosphere and the ocean is a problem of human behaviour.

As Manuel Barange, director of the Global Ocean Ecosystem Dynamics program based in Plymouth, puts it, humans have unwittingly become an intrinsic part of the marine system. The future is in our hands. It strikes me as critically important that we understand this.

Monica Sharma, a physician who works with the United Nations, delves deep into the human psyche to shift behaviour on seemingly intractable problems such as the practice of female genital mutilation and the spread of HIV/AIDS. I ran into her in New York recently. Her view is that for transformation to happen, we first need to understand that transformation is possible. And for that to happen, we need to strip ourselves psychologically naked and figure out what each of us stands for. What is the story about the world that makes sense to us emotionally? What is it that we believe? What are we here for?

Once we know that, we can start to ask the right questions, including: what's missing? Answering that question leads to a course of action.

When Sharma sits down with religious and community leaders whose culture tells them that girls must be genitally mutilated, she doesn't judge them or tell them that they're wrong or tell them what to do. She asks them what they stand for. It takes days of deep discussion. It is very hard work.

Once they can articulate where they stand or what their story is—she invites them to start asking questions, such as whether a practice such as female genital mutilation fits. If not, then why are they insisting it be done? She gives them the great gift of seeing the space between what they are and what they do. In many cases these leaders go back to their communities and stop the harm to their children.

A key to her success is that she doesn't give a prescription. Instead, she helps unleash imagination and creativity. In Africa, communities she and others have worked with have come up with more than 5000 different ways of combatting the spread of HIV/AIDS. The power is in the lack of dogma, in starting with the story, in honouring confusion, discomfort and fear. Sharma refers to this as a call for wisdom.

Here's my question, at the end of this long journey. *What do you stand for? What story do you tell yourself about why you're here?* Perhaps you are a hero. It's clear the world needs heroes right now to ask what's missing and how that can be made right. I don't know exactly how the heroes will gather and how they will alter the course of the planet's future—nobody does at this point, except that it will have to do with carbon dioxide concentrations in the atmosphere—but I know that if enough people are asking the right questions, we can make a start. This is a call for wisdom, not for logic; for hope rather than despair. It is about taking a stand and then acting on it—being fully human at a time when we need it most.

There's another piece to this. Many of the scientists I interviewed talked about the time frame of 2015 to 2030 as the drop-dead point for action that is effective for halting the planet's course toward chaos. Others are clear that if the carbon dioxide concentration in the atmosphere rises above 450 parts per million by volume, that will represent a point of no return. Today, it is 387 and rising faster than at any time since humans appeared on the planet.

If you believe that this matters and that something can be done, then the rest of the story reads that the time to act is right now.

SELECT BIBLIOGRAPHY

General reference books

Ballard, Robert D., and Michael Sweeney. *Return to Titanic*. Washington, DC: National Geographic, 2004.

Ballard, Robert D., and Will Hively. *The Eternal Darkness: A Personal History of Deep-Sea Exploration*. Princeton: Princeton University Press, 2000.

Borgese, Elisabeth Mann. *The Oceanic Circle*. Tokyo: United Nations University Press, 1999.

Burnie, David. *Concise Encyclopedia of the Human Body*. New York: Dorling Kindersley, 1997.

Burnie, David. *Dictionary of Nature*. Vancouver: Raincoast Books, 1994.

Cahill, Thomas. *Mysteries of the Middle Ages: The Rise of Feminism, Science, and Art from the Cults of Catholic Europe*. New York: Nan A. Talese, 2006.

Carson, Rachel. *The Sea Around Us*. London: Oxford University Press, 1951.

Chatwin, Bruce. *Songlines*. London: Random House UK, 2008.

Cousteau, Jean-Michel. *Mon Père, le Commandant*. Paris: l'Archipel, 2004.

Darwin, Charles. *Charles Darwin's Beagle Diary*. New York: Cambridge University Press, 2001.

Darwin, Charles. *The Origin of Species by Means of Natural Selection: The Preservation of Favoured Races in the Struggle for Life*. London: Penguin Classics, 1982.

Denny, Mark. *Air and Water: The Biology and Physics of Life's Media*. Princeton: Princeton University Press, 1995.

Ellis, Richard. *Aquagenesis: The Origin and Evolution of Life in the Sea*. Boston: Penguin, 2003.

Estes, James. *Whales, Whaling, and Ocean Ecosystems*. Berkeley: University of California Press, 2007.

Feynman, Richard P. *The Pleasure of Finding Things Out: The Best Short Works of Richard P. Feynman*. New York: Basic Books, 2000.

Feynman, Richard P., and Matthew L. Sands. *Six Easy Pieces: Essentials of Physics Explained by Its Most Brilliant Teacher*. New York: Perseus Books Group, 1996.

Flannery, Tim. *The Weather Makers: How We Are Changing the Climate and What It Means for Life on Earth*. Sydney: Allen Lane, 2006.

Francis, Clare, and Warren Tute. *The Commanding Sea*. London: British Broadcasting Corporation and Pelham Books, 1981.

German Advisory Council on Global Change. *The Future Oceans— Warming Up, Rising High, Turning Sour: Special Report*. Berlin: German Advisory Council on Global Change Secretariat, 2006.

'4th Global Conference on Oceans, Coasts, and Islands.' www. globaloceans.org/globalconferences/2008/index.html (accessed May 24, 2008).

Gore, Al. *An Inconvenient Truth: The Planetary Emergency of Global Warming and What We Can Do About It.* Emmaus, Pennsylvania: Rodale Books, 2006.

Holm, Poul. *The Exploited Seas: New Directions for Marine Environmental History.* St John's, Newfoundland: Census of Marine Life, 2001.

Hume, Stephen Eaton, Betty C. Keller, Otto Langer, Rosella M. Leslie, Alexandra Morton, and Don Staniford. *A Stain Upon the Sea: West Coast Salmon Farming.* Madeira Park, BC: Harbour Publishing, 2005.

Huntington, Ellsworth, and Stephen Sargent Visher. *Climatic Changes: Their Nature and Causes.* New Haven: Yale University Press, 1922.

'IISD RS summary of the 4th Global Conference on Oceans, Coasts and Islands Bulletin, 8–11 April 2008, Hanoi, Viet Nam.' International Institute for Sustainable Development, Reporting Services (IISD RS), 'Linkages'—A Multimedia Resource for Environment and Development Negotiations. www.iisd.ca/ymb/ sdoh4/ymb/ymbvol68num4e.html (accessed May 24, 2008).

Intergovernmental Panel on Climate Change. 'Intergovernmental Panel on Climate Change, Fourth Assessment Report.' www. ipcc.ch/ipccreports/ar4-syr.htm (accessed May 26, 2008).

King, Roger J.B., and Mike W. Robins. *Cancer Biology (3rd Edition).* Harlow, Essex: Pearson Educational Limited, 2006.

Kunzig, Robert. *Mapping the Deep: The Extraordinary Story of Ocean Science.* New York: W.W. Norton & Company, 2000.

Leier, Manfred. *World Atlas of the Oceans*. Toronto: Key Porter Books, 2000.

Levitin, Daniel J. *This Is Your Brain on Music: The Science of a Human Obsession*. New York: Plume, 2007.

Lovelock, James. *The Revenge of Gaia: Why the Earth is Fighting Back—and How We Can Still Save Humanity*. New York: Allen Lane, 2006.

Maas, Terry, and David Sipperly. *Freedive!* New York: Bluewater Freedivers, 1998.

McCullough, David. *The Path Between the Seas: The Creation of the Panama Canal, 1870–1914*. New York, NY: Simon & Schuster, 1978.

MacInnis, Joe. *James Cameron's Aliens of the Deep: Voyages to the Strange World of the Deep Ocean*. Washington DC: National Geographic, 2005.

Magnus, Olaus, and P.G. Foote. *A Description of the Northern Peoples, 1555 3 Volumes (Hakluyt Society Second Ser., Nos. 182, 187, 188)*. London: Hakluyt Society, 1996.

Mitchell, Alanna. *Dancing at the Dead Sea: Tracking the World's Environmental Hotspots*. Chicago: University Of Chicago Press, 2005.

Muecke, Stephen, and Adam Shoemaker. *Aboriginal Australians: First Nations of an Ancient Continent*. London: Thames & Hudson Ltd, 2004.

Nouvian, Claire. *The Deep: The Extraordinary Creatures of the Abyss*. Chicago: University of Chicago Press, 2007.

Parker, K. Langloh. *Wise Women of the Dreamtime: Aboriginal Tales of the Ancestral Powers*. Rochester: Park Street Press, 1993.

Ponting, Clive. *A Green History of the World: The Environment and the Collapse of Great Civilizations*. Boston: Penguin, 1993.

Reed, A.W. *Aboriginal Myths: Tales of the Dreamtime*. Seattle: Reed Natural History Australia, 1998.

Russell, Dick. *Eye of the Whale: Epic Passage from Baja to Siberia*. New York: Simon & Schuster, 2001.

Short, John Rennie. *The World through Maps: A History of Cartography*. Toronto: Firefly Books, 2003.

Silvertown, Jonathan. *Demons in Eden: The Paradox of Plant Diversity*. Chicago: University of Chicago Press, 2005.

Steffen, W. *Global Change and the Earth System: A Planet Under Pressure (Global Change — The IGBP Series)*. New York: Springer, 2005.

Stern, Sir Nicholas. 'Stern Review on the Economics of Climate Change.' HM Treasury. www.hm-treasury.gov.uk/independent_reviews/stern review_economics_climate_change/sternreview_index.cfm (accessed May 24, 2008).

Stewart, Iain. *Journeys from the Centre of the Earth: How Geology Shaped Civilization*. London: Century, 2005.

Stow, Dorrik. *Oceans: An Illustrated Reference*. Chicago: University of Chicago Press, 2006.

Suzuki, David, and Amanda McConnell. *The Sacred Balance: Rediscovering Our Place in Nature*. Seattle: Mountaineers Books, 2002.

Tidwell, Mike. *Bayou Farewell: The Rich Life and Tragic Death of Louisiana's Cajun Coast*. New York: Vintage, 2004.

Valiela, Ivan. *Global Coastal Change*. Malden, Massachusetts: Wiley-Blackwell, 2006.

Weisman, Alan. *The World Without Us*. New York: Thomas Dunne Books, 2007.

Wilson, Edward O. *The Future of Life*. New York: Knopf, 2002.

Wilson, Edward O. *Consilience: The Unity of Knowledge*. New York: Knopf, 1998.

Young, J.Z. *The Life of Vertebrates*. Oxford: Clarendon Press, 1991.

Selected coral references

Brodie, J., K. Fabricius, G. De'ath, and K. Okaji. 'Are increased nutrient inputs responsible for more outbreaks of crown-of-thorns starfish? An appraisal of the evidence.' *Marine Pollution Bulletin* 51 (2005): pp. 266–278.

Bruno, John F., and Elizabeth R. Selig. 'Regional decline of coral cover in the Indo-Pacific: timing, extent, and subregional comparisons.' *PLoS ONE* 2 (2007): e711.

'Coral Reefs and Climate Change.' *Australian Institute of Marine Science Briefing Paper*, 1 February, 2006.

Doebeli, Michael, and Nancy Knowlton. 'The evolution of interspecific mutualisms.' *PNAS* 95 (1998): pp. 8676–8680.

Donner, Simon D., and David Potere. 'The inequity of the global threat to coral reefs: viewpoint.' *BioScience* 57 (2007): pp. 214–215.

'Effects of Terrestrial Runoff of Sediments, Nutrients and Other Pollutants on Coral Reefs.' *International Society for Reef Studies* Briefing Paper 3 (2004).

Fabricius, K.E. 'Effects of terrestrial runoff on the ecology of corals and coral reefs: review and synthesis.' *Marine Pollution Bulletin* 50 (2005): pp. 125–146.

Fabricius, Katharina, and Glenn De'ath. 'Identifying ecological change and its causes: a case study on coral reefs.' *Ecological Applications* 14 (2004): pp. 1448–1465.

Fukami, Hironobu, Ann F. Budd, Don R. Levitan, Javier Jara, Ralf Kersanach, and Nancy Knowlton. 'Geographic differences in species boundaries among members of the *Montastraea annularis* complex based on molecular and morphological markers.' *Evolution* 58 (2004): pp. 324–337.

Fukami, Hironobu. 'Conventional taxonomy obscures deep divergence between Pacific and Atlantic corals.' *Nature* 427 (2004): pp. 832–835.

Grimsditch, Gabriel D., and Rodney V. Salm. *Coral Reef Resilience and Resistance to Bleaching.* Gland, Switzerland: The World Conservation Union (IUCN), 2005.

Hoegh-Guldberg, O., et al. 'Coral reefs under rapid climate change and ocean acidification.' *Science* 318 (2007): pp. 1737-1742.

Jackson, Jeremy B.C. 'Ecological extinction and evolution in the brave new ocean.' *PNAS* 105 (2008): pp. 11458-11465.

Johnson, J.E., and P.A. Marshall (eds). *Climate Change and the Great Barrier Reef.* Australia: Great Barrier Reef Marine Park Authority and Australian Greenhouse Office, 2007.

Knowlton, Nancy. 'Multiple "stable" states and the conservation of marine ecosystems.' *Progress in Oceanography* 60 (2004): pp. 387–396.

Knowlton, Nancy. 'Who are the players on coral reefs and does it matter? The importance of coral taxonomy for coral reef management.' *Bulletin of Marine Science* 69 (2001): pp. 305–308.

Knowlton, Nancy. 'The future of coral reefs: colloquium.' *PNAS* 98 (2001): pp. 5419–5425.

Knowlton, Nancy, Judith C. Lang, M. Christine Ronney, and Patricia Clifford. 'Evidence for delayed mortality in hurricane-damaged Jamaican staghorn corals.' *Nature* 294 (1981): pp. 251–252.

'Last Days of the Ocean.' *Mother Jones*, March–April 2006.

Levitan, Don R., et al. 'Mechanisms of reproductive isolation among sympatric broadcast-spawning corals of the *Montastraea annularis* species complex.' *Evolution* 58 (2004): pp. 308–323.

Roberts, Santi, and Michael Hirshfield. 'Deep-sea corals: out of sight, but no longer out of mind.' *Frontiers in Ecology and the Environment* 2 (2004): pp. 123–130.

Royal Society, The. *Ocean Acidification due to Increasing Atmospheric Carbon Dioxide Policy Document 12 / 05*. London: The Royal Society, 2005.

Sala, E., and N. Knowlton. 'Global marine biodiversity trends.' *Annual Review of the Environment and Resources* 31 (2006): pp. 93–122.

'The State of the Marine Environment: Trends and Processes.' United Nations Environment Programme, Global Programme of Action for the Protection of the Marine Environment from Land-Based Activities. www.gpa.unep.org/documents/soe_trends_and_english.pdf (accessed May 25, 2008).

Veron, J.E.N. *A Reef in Time: The Great Barrier Reef from Beginning to End*. Cambridge: Belknap Press, 2008.

Wilkinson, Clive. *Status of Coral Reefs of the World: 2004*. Townsville, Queensland: Australian Institute of Marine Science, 2004.

Selected anoxia/hypoxia papers

An Assessment of Coastal Hypoxia and Eutrophication in US Waters. Washington, DC: National Science and Technology Council Committee on Environment and Natural Resources, 2003.

Breitburg, Denise. 'Effects of hypoxia, and the balance between hypoxia and enrichment, on coastal fishes and fisheries.' *Estuaries* 14 (2002): pp. 1448–1465.

Chan, F., J.A. Barth, J. Lubchenco, H. Weeks, W.T. Peterson, and B.A. Menge. 'Emergence of anoxia in the California current large marine ecosystem.' *Science* 319 (2008): p. 920.

Diaz, Robert J. 'Overview of hypoxia around the world.' *Journal of Environmental Quality* 3 (2001): pp. 275–281.

Diaz, Robert J., and Rutger Rosenberg. 'Spreading dead zones and consequences for marine ecosystems.' *Science* 321 (2008): pp. 926-929.

Ferber, Dan. 'Keeping the stygian waters at bay.' *Science* 291 (2001): pp. 968–973.

Hotinski, Roberta M., et al. 'Ocean stagnation and end-Permian anoxia.' *Geology* 29:1 (2001): pp. 7–10.

Integrated Assessment of Hypoxia in the Northern Gulf of Mexico. Washington, DC: National Science and Technology Council Committee on Environment and Natural Resources, 2000.

Joyce, Stephanie. 'The dead zones: oxygen-starved coastal waters.' *Environmental Health Perspectives* 108 (2000): pp. 120–125.

Justic, Dubravko, Nancy N. Rabalais, and R. Eugene Turner. 'Coupling between climate variability and coastal eutrophication: Evidence and outlook for the northern Gulf of Mexico.' *Journal of Sea Research* 54 (2005): pp. 25–35.

Justic, Dubravko, Nancy N. Rabalais, and R. Eugene Turner. 'Modeling the impacts of decadal changes in riverine nutrient fluxes on coastal eutrophication near the Mississippi River delta.' *Ecological Modelling* 152 (2002): pp. 33–46.

Justic, Dubravko, Nancy N. Rabalais, and R. Eugene Turner. 'Impacts of climate change on net productivity of coastal waters: implications for carbon budgets and hypoxia.' *Climate Research* 8 (1997): pp. 225–237.

Justic, Dubravko, Nancy N. Rabalais, and R. Eugene Turner. 'Effects of climate change on hypoxia in coastal waters: A doubled CO_2 scenario for the northern Gulf of Mexico.' *Limnological Oceanography* 41 (1996): pp. 992–1003.

Neretin, L.N. *Past and Present Water Column Anoxia*. The Netherlands: Springer, 2006.

Pelley, Janet. 'Is coastal eutrophication out of control?' *Environmental Science & Technology* October 1 (1998): pp. 462–466.

Platon, Emil, Barun K. Sen Gupta, Nancy N. Rabalais, and R. Eugene Turner. 'Effect of seasonal hypoxia on the benthic foraminiferal community of the Louisiana inner continental shelf: the 20th century record.' *Marine Micropaleontology* 54 (2005): pp. 263–283.

Pocock, John. 'Chokehold on farm nutrients? Washington looks to the nation's agricultural midsection to solve environmental degradation in the Gulf of Mexico.' *The Farmer/Dakota Farmer* September (1999): pp. 14–33.

Rabalais, Nancy N., Nazan Atilla, Claire Normandeau, and R. Eugene Turner. 'Ecosystem history of Mississippi River-influenced continental shelf revealed through preserved phytoplankton pigments.' *Marine Pollution Bulletin* 49 (2004): pp. 537–547.

Rabalais, Nancy N., R. Eugene Turner, and Donald Scavia.

'Beyond science into policy: Gulf of Mexico hypoxia and the Mississippi River.' *BioScience* 52 (2002): pp. 129–142.

Rabalais, Nancy N. 'Nitrogen in aquatic ecosystems.' *Ambio* 31 (2002): pp. 102–112.

Rabalais, Nancy N., R. Eugene Turner, Quay Dortch, William J. Wiseman, Jr., and Barun K. Sen Gupta. 'Nutrient changes in the Mississippi River and system responses on the adjacent continental shelf.' *Estuaries* 19 (1996): pp. 386–407.

Sen Gupta, Barun K., R. Eugene Turner, and Nancy N. Rabalais. 'Seasonal oxygen depletion in continental-shelf waters of Louisiana: historical record of benthic foraminifers.' *Geology* 24 (1996): p. 227.

Turner, R.E., N.N. Rabalais, and D. Justic. 'Predicting summer hypoxia in the northern Gulf of Mexico: riverine N, P, and Si loading.' *Marine Pollution Bulletin* 52 (2006): pp. 132–148.

Turner, R. Eugene, Nancy N. Rabalais, Dubravko Justic, and Quay Dortch. 'Future aquatic nutrient limitations.' *Marine Pollution Bulletin* 46 (2003): pp. 1032–1034.

Turner, R. Eugene, and Nancy N. Rabalais. 'Linking landscape and water quality in the Mississippi River basin for 200 years.' *BioScience* 53 (2003): pp. 563–572.

Turner, R.E., N.N. Rabalais, D. Justic, and Q. Dortch. 'Global patterns of dissolved N, P and Si in large rivers.' *Biogeochemistry* 64 (2003): pp. 297–317.

Turner, R. Eugene, and Nancy N. Rabalais. 'Coastal eutrophication near the Mississippi River delta.' *Nature* 368 (1994): pp. 619–621.

Turner, R. Eugene, and Nancy N. Rabalais. 'Changes in Mississippi River water quality this century: implications for coastal food webs.' *BioScience* 41 (1991): pp. 140–147.

Selected ocean pH papers

Caldeira, Ken, and Michael E. Wickett. 'Ocean model predictions of chemistry changes from carbon dioxide emissions to the atmosphere and ocean.' *Journal of Geophysical Research* 110 (2005).

Caldeira, Ken, and Michael E. Wickett. 'Anthropogenic carbon and ocean pH.' *Nature* 425 (2003): p. 365.

Doney, S.C., and K. Lindsay, et al. 'Evaluating global ocean carbon models: The importance of realistic physics.' *Geophysical Research Letters* 18 (2004).

Feely, Richard A., et al. 'Impact of anthropogenic CO_2 on the $CaCO_3$ system in the oceans.' *Science* 305 (2004): pp. 362–366.

Gattuso, J-P, M. Frankignoulle, I. Bourge, S. Romaine, and R.W. Buddemeier. 'Effect of calcium carbonate saturation of seawater on coral calcification.' *Global and Planetary Change* 18 (1998): pp. 37–46.

Hughes, T.P., A.H. Baird, J.M. Louh, P. Marshall, M. Nystrom, S.R. Palumbi, J.M. Pandolfi, B. Rosen, J. Roughgarden, D.R. Bellwood, M. Card, S.R. Connolly, C. Folke, R. Grosberg, O. Hoegh-Guldberg, J.B.C. Jackson, and J. Kleypas, et al. 'Climate change, human impacts, and the resilience of coral reefs.' *Science* 301 (2003): pp. 929–933.

Kleypas, J.A., et al. 'Impacts of Ocean Acidification on Coral Reefs and Other Marine Calcifiers: A Guide for Future Research.' Report of a workshop held on 18–20 April 2005, St Petersburg, Florida, sponsored by NSF, NOAA, and the US Geological Survey.

Kleypas, J.A., R.W. Buddemeier, and J-P Gattuso. 'The future of coral reefs in an age of global change.' *International Journal of Earth Sciences* 90 (2001): pp. 426–437.

Kleypas, J.A., and C. Langdon. 'Overview of CO_2-induced changes in seawater chemistry.' *Proceedings of the 9th International Coral Reef Symposium, Bali, Indonesia, 23–27 Oct 2000* 2 (2000): pp. 1087–1089.

Kleypas, J.A., R.W. Buddemeier, D. Archer, J-P Gattuso, C. Langdon, and B.N. Opdyke. 'Geochemical consequences of increased atmospheric CO_2 on coral reefs.' *Science* 284 (1999): pp. 118–120.

Kolbert, Elizabeth. 'The darkening sea: What carbon emissions are doing to the ocean.' *The New Yorker* (November 20, 2006): pp. 65–75.

Kuffner, Ilsa B., Andreas J. Andersson, Paul L. Jokiel, Ku'Ulei S. Rodgers, and Fred T. Mackenzie. 'Decreased abundance of crustose coralline algae due to ocean acidification.' *Nature Geoscience* 1 (2007): pp. 114–117.

Langdon, C., T. Takahashi, C. Sweeney, D. Chipman, J. Goddard, F. Marubini, H. Aceves, H. Barnett, and M.J. Atkinson. 'Effect of calcium carbonate saturation state on the calcification rate of an experimental coral reef.' *Global Biogeochemical Cycles* 14 (2000): pp. 639–654.

Orr, James C., et al. 'Anthropogenic ocean acidification over the twenty-first century and its impact on calcifying organisms.' *Nature* 437 (2005).

Phinney, J.T., O. Hoegh-Guldberg, J. Kleypas, W. Skirving, and A. Strong. *Coral Reefs and Climate Change: Science and Management.* Washington, DC: AGU Monograph Series, Coastal and Estuarine Studies, American Geophysical Union, vol. 61, 2006.

Royal Society, The. *Ocean Acidification due to Increasing Atmospheric Carbon Dioxide Policy Document 12/05.* London, UK: The Royal Society, 2005.

Sarmiento, J.L., et al. 'Response of ocean ecosystems to climate warming.' *Global Biogeochemical Cycles* 18 (2004).

Scheibner, C., and R.P. Speijer. 'Decline of coral reefs during late Paleocene to early Eocene global warming.' *Earth*. 2 (2007): pp. 133–150, www.electronic-earth-discuss.net/2/133/2007.

Selected plankton references

'Annual Report Card 2007.' United Kingdom Marine Climate Change Impacts Partnership (MCCIP). www.mccip.org.uk/arc (accessed May 25, 2008).

Attrill, Martin J., Jade Wright, and Martin Edwards. 'Climate-related increases in jellyfish frequency suggest a more gelatinous future for the North Sea.' *Limnology and Oceanography* 52 (2007): pp. 480–485.

Beaugrand, Gregory, Philip C. Reid, Frederic Ibanez, J. Alistair Lindley, and Martin Edwards. 'Reorganization of North Atlantic marine copepod biodiversity and climate.' *Science* 296 (2002): pp. 1692–1694.

Burkill, P.H. (guest editor). 'Arabesque: UK JGOFS process studies in the Arabian Sea.' *Topical Studies in Oceanography: Deep Sea Research Part ii* 46 (1999).

Chisholm, Sallie W., and Francois M.M. Morel (eds). 'What controls phytoplankton production in nutrient-rich areas of the open sea?' *Limnology and Oceanography* 36 (1991).

Edwards, M., D.G. Johns, et al. 'Regional climate change and harmful algal blooms in the northeast Atlantic.' *Limnology and Oceanography* 51 (2006): pp. 820–829.

Edwards, M., D.G. Johns, P. Licandro, A.W.G. John, and D.P. Stevens. 'Ecological status 2004/2005: results from the North

Atlantic CPR survey.' *SAHFOS Technical Report* 3 (2004): pp. 1–8.

Edwards, Martin, and Anthony J. Richardson. 'Impact of climate change on marine pelagic phenology and trophic mismatch.' *Nature* 430 (2004): pp. 881–884.

Falkowski, Paul, and Andrew Knoll (eds). *Evolution of Primary Producers in the Sea*. Toronto: Academic Press, 2007.

Frederiksen, Morten, Martin Edwards, Anthony J. Richardson, Nicholas C. Halliday, and Sarah Wanless. 'From plankton to top predators: bottom-up control of a marine food web across four trophic levels.' *Journal of Animal Ecology* (2006).

Genner, Martin J., David W. Sims, et al. 'Regional climatic warming drives long-term community changes of British marine fish.' *Proceedings of the Royal Society of London* 271 (2004): pp. 655–661.

Hawkins, Stephen J., Alan J. Southward and Martin J. Genner. 'Detection of environmental change in a marine ecosystem— evidence from the western English Channel.' *Science of the Total Environment* 310 (2003): pp. 245–256.

Herbert, R.J.H., S.J. Hawkins, M. Sheader and A.J. Southward. 'Range extension and reproduction of the barnacle *Balanus perforatus* in the eastern English Channel.' *Journal of the Marine Biological Association of the United Kingdom* 83 (2003): pp. 73–82.

Iglesias-Rodriguez, M. Debora, et al. 'Representing key phytoplankton functional groups in ocean carbon cycle models: cocco‑lithophorids.' *Global Biogeochemical Cycles* 16 (2002).

Lopez-Urrutia, Angel, Elena San Martin, Roger P. Harris, and Xabier Irigoien. 'Scaling the metabolic balance of the oceans.' *PNAS* 103 (2006): pp. 8739–8744.

Owens, N.J.P., et al. 'Methane flux to the atmosphere from the Arabian Sea.' *Nature* 354 (1991): pp. 293–296.

Pitois, S., and C.J. Fox. 'Detecting changes in long-term zooplankton abundance and size structure in the North Atlantic.' *ICES Journal of Marine Science* 63 (2006): pp. 785–798.

Portner, Hans O., and Rainer Knust. 'Climate change affects marine fishes through the oxygen limitation of thermal tolerance.' *Science* 315 (2007): pp. 95–97.

Raitsos, Dionysios E., Philip C. Reid, Samantha Lavender, Martin Edwards, and Anthony J. Richardson. 'Extending the SeaWiFS chlorophyll data set back 50 years in the northeast Atlantic.' *Geophysical Research Letters* 32 (2005).

Reid, P.C., J.M. Colebrook, J.B.L. Matthews, and J. Aiken. 'The continuous plankton recorder: concepts and history, from plankton indicator to undulating recorders.' *Progress in Oceanography* 58 (2003): pp. 117–173.

Richardson, A.J., and A.W. Walne. 'Using continuous plankton recorder data.' *Progress in Oceanography* 68 (2006): pp. 27–74.

Ridgwell, A., and J.C. Hargreaves, et al. 'Marine geochemical data assimilation in an efficient earth system model of global biogeochemical cycling.' *Biogeosciences* 4 (2007): pp. 87–104.

Ridgwell, Andy J., Mark A. Maslin, and Andrew J. Watson. 'Reduced effectiveness of terrestrial carbon sequestration due to an antagonistic response of ocean productivity.' *Geophysical Research Letters* 29 (2002).

Rusch, Douglas B., et al. 'The Sorcerer II global ocean sampling expedition: northwest Atlantic through eastern tropical Pacific.' *PLoS Biology* 5 (2007): p. 34.

Rutherford, Scott, Steven D'Hondt and Warren Prell. 'Environmental controls on the geographic distribution of zooplankton diversity.' *Nature* 400 (1999): pp. 749–753.

Southward, Alan J., et al. 'Long-term oceanographic and ecological research in the western English Channel.' *Advances in Marine Biology* 47.

Springer, A.M., et al. 'Sequential megafaunal collapse in the North Pacific Ocean: An ongoing legacy of industrial whaling.' *PNAS* 100 (2003): pp. 12223–12228.

Selected papers on fish

Berkes, F., T.P. Hughes, R.S. Steneck, J.A. Wilson, D.R. Bellwood, B. Crona, C. Folke, L.H. Gunderson, H.M. Leslie, and J. Norberg, M. Nystrom, P. Olsson, H. Osterblom, M. Scheffer, B. Worm, 'Globalization, roving bandits, and marine resources.' *Science* 311 (2006): pp. 1557–1558.

Boddeke, R., and B. Vingerhoed. 'The anchovy returns to the Wadden Sea.' *ICES Journal of Marine Science* 53 (1996): pp. 1003–1007.

Devine, Jennifer A., Krista D. Baker, and Richard L. Haedrich. 'Fisheries: Deep-sea fishes qualify as endangered.' *Nature* 439 (2006).

Hoffmann, R.C. 'A brief history of aquatic resource use in medieval Europe.' *Helgoland Marine Research* 59 (2005): pp. 22–30.

Hutchings, Jeffrey A., and Ransom A. Myers. 'What can be learned from the collapse of a renewable resource? Atlantic cod, *Gadus morhua*, of Newfoundland and Labrador.' *Canadian Journal of Fisheries and Aquatic Sciences* 51 (1994): pp. 2126–2146.

Hutchings, Jeffrey A. 'Collapse and recovery of marine fishes.' *Nature* 406 (2000): pp. 882–885.

Hutchings, Jeffrey A. 'Spatial and temporal variation in the density of northern cod and a review of hypotheses for the stock's collapse.' *Canadian Journal of Fisheries and Aquatic Sciences* 53 (1996): pp. 943–962.

Lotze, Heike. 'Rise and fall of fishing and marine resource use in the Wadden Sea, southern North Sea.' *Fisheries Research* 87 (2007): pp. 208–218.

Lotze, Heike, et al. 'Depletion, degradation, and recovery potential of estuaries and coastal seas.' *Science* 312 (2006): pp. 1806–1809.

Lotze, Heike, and Karsten Reise (eds). *Helgoland Marine Research, vol. 59, no. 1, April 2005*. Bremerhaven, Germany: Springer-Verlag Berlin Heidelberg and Alfred Wegener Institute for Polar and Marine Research, 2005.

Lotze, Heike K. 'Repetitive history of resource depletion and mismanagement: the need for a shift in perspective.' *Marine Ecology Progress Series* 274 (2004): pp. 282–285.

Lotze, Heike, and Inka Milewski. 'Two centuries of multiple human impacts and successive changes in a North Atlantic food web.' *Ecological Applications* 14 (2004): pp. 1428–1447.

Myers, Ransom A., and Boris Worm. 'Rapid worldwide depletion of predatory fish communities.' *Nature* 423 (2003): 280–283.

'Olaus Magnus Map.' Bell Library Index. http://bell.lib.umn.edu/olaus/ (accessed May 26, 2008).

Pauly, Daniel. 'Major trends in small-scale marine fisheries, with emphasis on developing countries, and some implications for the social sciences.' *MAST* 4 (2006): pp. 7–22.

Pauly, Daniel, and Maria-Lourdes Palomares. 'Fishing down marine food web: it is far more pervasive than we thought.' *Bulletin of Marine Science* 76 (2005): pp. 197–212.

Pauly, Daniel, Jackie Alder, Elena Bennett, Villy Christensen, Peter Tyedmers, and Reg Watson. 'The future for fisheries.' *Science* 302 (2003): pp. 1359–1361.

Pauly, Daniel, and Reg Watson. 'Counting the last fish.' *Scientific American* 289 (2003): pp. 42–47.

Rosenberg, Andrew A., et al. 'The history of ocean resources: modeling cod biomass using historical records.' *Frontiers in Ecology and the Environment* 3 (2005): pp. 84–90.

Schrope, Mark. 'Oceanography: the real sea change.' *Nature* 443 (2006): pp. 622–624.

State of World Fisheries and Aquaculture, 2006. Rome: Food and Agriculture Organization of the United Nations, 2006.

Sumaila, U.R. and D. Pauly (eds). *Catching More Bait: A Bottom-Up Re-estimation of Global Fisheries Subsidies*. Fisheries Centre Research Reports 14:6 (2006), 2nd version. Vancouver, British Columbia: University of British Columbia.

Ward, Peter, and Ransom A. Myers. 'Shifts in open-ocean fish communities coinciding with the commencement of commercial fishing.' *Ecology* 86 (2005): pp. 835–847.

Worm, B, E.B. Barbier, N. Beaumont, J.E. Duffy, C Folke, B.S. Halpern, J.B.C. Jackson, H.K. Lotze, F. Micheli, and S.R. Palumbi, E. Sala, K.A. Selkoe, J.J. Stachowicz, R. Watson. 'Impacts of biodiversity loss on ocean ecosystem services.' *Science* 314 (2006): pp. 787–790.

Worm, Boris, Heike K. Lotze, and Ransom A. Myers. 'Predator diversity hotspots in the blue ocean.' *PNAS* 100 (2003): pp. 9884–9888.

Worm, Boris, Marcel Sandow, Andreas Oschlies, Heike Lotze, and Ransom A. Myers. 'Global patterns of predator diversity in the open oceans.' *Science* 309 (2005): pp. 1365–1369.

Zeller, Dirk, and Daniel Pauly. 'Good news, bad news: global fisheries discards are declining, but so are total catches.' *Fish and Fisheries* 6 (2005): pp. 156–159.

Selected ocean and climate change papers

Berman, J. Michael, Kevin R. Arrigo, and Pamela A. Matson. 'Agricultural runoff fuels large phytoplankton blooms in vulnerable areas of the ocean.' *Nature* 434 (2005): pp. 211–214.

Boyer, Timothy B., S. Levitus, J.I. Antonov, R.A. Locarnini, and H.E. Garcia. 'Linear trends in salinity for the World Ocean 1995–1998.' *Geophysical Research Letters* 32 (2005).

Boyle, Edward A. 'Characteristics of the deep ocean carbon system during the past 150,000 years.' *PNAS* 94 (1997): pp. 8300–8307.

Buermann, Wolfgang, Benjamin R. Lintner, Charles D. Koven, Alon Angert, Jorge E. Pinzon, Compton J. Tucker, and Inez Y. Fung. 'The changing carbon cycle at Mauna Loa Observatory.' *PNAS* 104 (2007): pp. 4249–4254.

Canadell, Josep, and Corinne Le Quere, et al. 'Contributions to accelerating atmospheric CO_2 growth from economic activity, carbon intensity, and efficiency of natural sinks.' *PNAS* 104 (2007): pp. 18866–18870.

Corredor, Jorge E., and Julio M. Morell. 'Seasonal variation of physical and biogeochemical features in eastern Caribbean surface water.' *Journal of Geophysical Research* 106 (2001): pp. 4517–4525.

Curry, Ruth, Bob Dickson and Igor Yashayaev. 'A change in the freshwater balance of the Atlantic Ocean over the past four decades.' *Nature* 426 (2003): pp. 826–829.

Dickson, Bob, et al. 'Rapid freshening of the deep North Atlantic Ocean over the past four decades.' *Nature* 416 (2002): pp. 832–837.

Friedlingstein, Pierre, and Susan Solomon. 'Contributions of past and present human generations to committed warming caused by carbon dioxide.' *PNAS* 102 (2005): pp. 10832–10836.

Galloway, James N. 'The nitrogen cascade.' *BioScience* 53 (2003): pp. 341–356.

Goreau, Thomas J., Raymond L. Hayes, and Don McAllister. 'Regional patterns of sea surface temperature rise: implications for global ocean circulation change and the future of coral reefs and fisheries.' *World Resource Review* 17 (2005): pp. 350–373.

Govindasamy, B., S. Thompson, A. Mirin, M. Wickett, K. Caldeira, and C. Delire. 'Increase of carbon cycle feedback with climate sensitivity: results from a coupled climate and carbon cycle model.' *Tellus* 57B (2005): pp. 153–163.

Halpern, Benjamin, et al. 'A global map of human impact on marine ecosystems.' *Science* 319 (2008): pp. 948–952.

Mayhew, Peter J., Gareth B. Jenkins, and Timothy G. Benton. 'A long-term association between global temperature and biodiversity, origination and extinction in the fossil record.' *Proceedings of the Royal Society of London B* 275 (2008): pp. 47–54.

McLaughlin, John F., Jessica J. Hellmann, Carol L. Boggs, and Paul R. Ehrlich. 'Climate change hastens population extinctions.' *PNAS* 99 (2002): pp. 6070–6074.

Pahlow, Markus, and Ulf Riebesell. 'Temporal trends in deep ocean Redfield ratios.' *Science* 287 (2000): pp. 831–833.

Raupach, Michael, et al. 'Global and regional drivers of accelerating CO_2 emissions.' *PNAS* 104 (2007): pp. 10288–10293.

Scholze, Marko, Wolfgang Knorr, Nigel W. Arnell, and I. Colin Prentice. 'A climate-change risk analysis for world ecosystems.' *PNAS* 103 (2006): pp. 13116–13120.

Thompson, Richard C. 'Lost at sea: where is all the plastic?' *Science* 304 (2004): p. 838.

Williams, John W., Stephen T. Jackson, and John E. Kutzbach. 'Projected distributions of novel and disappearing climates by 2100 AD.' *PNAS* 104 (2007): pp. 5738–5742.

Selected papers on the Paleocene/Eocene Thermal Maximum

Brinkhuis, Henk, Stefan Schouten, Jonathan Bujak, Ruediger Stein, Johan Van Der Burgh, James S. Eldrett, Ian Harding, Andre Lotter, Francesca Sangiorgi, Han Van Konijnenburg-Van Cittert, Jan De Leeuw, Jens Matthiessen, Margaret Collinson, Jan Backman, Kathryn Moran, Appy Sluijs, Jaap S. Sinninghe Damste, Gerald Dickens, Matthew Huber, Thomas Cronin, Jonaotaro Onodera, and Kozo Takahashi. 'Episodic fresh surface waters in the Eocene Arctic Ocean.' *Nature* 441 (2006): pp. 606–609.

Huber, Matthew, and Rodrigo Caballero. 'Eocene El Niño: Evidence for robust tropical dynamics in the "hothouse."' *Science* 299 (2003): pp. 877–881.

Jaramillo, Carlos, Milton J. Rueda, and German Mora. 'Cenozoic plant diversity in the neotropics.' *Science* 311 (2006): pp. 1893–1896.

Kerr, Richard A. 'Global climate change: the Atlantic conveyor may have slowed, but don't panic yet.' *Science* 310 (2005): pp. 1403–1404.

Najjar, Raymond G., et al. 'Modeling geographic impacts on early Eocene ocean temperature.' *Geophysical Research Letters* 29 (2002).

Pagani, Mark, Ken Caldeira, David Archer, and James C. Zachos. 'An ancient carbon mystery.' *Science* 314 (2006): pp. 1556–1557.

Pagani, Mark. 'Arctic hydrology during global warming at the Palaeocene/Eocene thermal maximum.' *Nature* 442 (2006): pp. 671–675.

Pagani, Mark, James C. Zachos, Katherine H. Freeman, Brett Tipple, and Stephen Bohaty. 'Marked decline in atmospheric carbon dioxide concentrations during the Paleogene.' *Science* 309 (2005): pp. 600–603.

Pagani, Mark. 'The alkenone-CO_2 proxy and ancient atmospheric carbon dioxide.' *Philosophical Transactions of the Royal Society London A* 360 (2002): pp. 609–632.

Pagani, Mark, Michael A. Arthur, and Katherine H. Freeman. 'Variations in Miocene phytoplankton growth rates in the southwest Atlantic: evidence for changes in ocean circulation.' *Paleoceanography* 15 (2000): pp. 486–496.

Pagani, Mark, Michael A. Arthur, and Katherine H. Freeman. 'Miocene evolution of atmospheric carbon dioxide.' *Paleoceanography* 14 (1999): pp. 273–292.

Schmidt, Gavin A., and Drew T. Shindell. 'Atmospheric composition, radiative forcing, and climate change as a consequence of a massive methane release from gas hydrates.' *Paleoceanography* 18 (2003).

Schwartz, Peter, and Doug Randall. 'An Abrupt Climate Change Scenario and Its Implications for United States National Security: Imagining the Unthinkable, October 2003.' GBN Global Business Network. http://gbn.com (accessed May 27, 2008).

Sluijs, Appy, Stefan Schouten, Jens Matthiessen, Lucas Lourens, Nikolai Pedentchouk, Jan Backman, Kathryn Moran, Mark Pagani, Martijn Woltering, Henk Brinkhuis, Jaap S. Sinninghe Damste, Gerald Dickens, Matthew Huber, Gert-Jan Reichart, and Ruediger Stein. 'Subtropical Arctic Ocean temperatures during the Palaeocene/Eocene thermal maximum.' *Nature* 441 (2006): pp. 610–613.

Sriver, Ryan L., and Matthew Huber. 'Observational evidence for an ocean heat pump induced by tropical cyclones.' *Nature* 447 (2007): pp. 577–580.

Stoll, Heather. 'Climate change: the Arctic tells its story.' *Nature* 441 (2006): pp. 579–581.

Witze, Alexandra. 'Bad weather ahead.' *Nature* 441 (2006): pp. 564–566.

Zachos, James, Mark Pagani, Lisa Sloan, Ellen Thomas, and Katharina Billups. 'Trends, rhythms, and aberrations in global climate 65 Ma to Present.' *Science* 292 (2001): pp. 686–693.

Selected papers on China

CCICED, Secretariat of. 'President Hu Jintao expounds China's stance on climate change at APEC meeting.' *CCICED Update* 23 (2007).

China's National Climate Change Programme. Beijing: National Development and Reform Commissions, 2007.

Hanson, Arthur J., and Claude Martin. *One Lifeboat: China and the World's Environment and Development*. Winnipeg, Manitoba, Canada: International Institute for Sustainable Development, 2006.

Martinot, Eric, and Jungfeng Li. *Powering China's Development: The Role of Renewable Energy*. Washington, DC: Worldwatch Institute, 2007.

National Development and Reform Commission of China. 'National Climate Change Program.' China.org.cn (accessed June 4, 2007).

Sævarsson, Haflioi. *China Seafood Industry Report*. Shanghai: Glitnir Research Division, 2007.

State Council Information Office of China. 'White paper on energy.' China.org.cn (accessed December 26, 2007).

Wang, Hongying. 'China's changing approach to sustainable development.' *Development* 50 (2007): pp. 36–43.

World Energy Outlook 2007. Paris: International Energy Agency, 2007.

Selected papers on Zanzibar

Cohen, Ilana. *Mollusc collecting and Bivalve Farming: Economics and Strategies in Two Zanzibari Villages.* Stone Town, Zanzibar: School for International Training, Zanzibar, Tanzania, 2005.

Jiddawi, Narriman S., and Marcus C. Ohman. 'Marine fisheries in Tanzania.' *AMBIO: A Journal of the Human Environment* 31 (2002): pp. 518–527.

Kariger, Patricia K., et al. 'Iron deficiency and physical growth predict attainment of walking but not crawling in poorly nourished Zanzibari infants.' *The Journal of Nutrition* 135 (2005): pp. 814–819.

Richmond, M.D., and J. Francis. *Marine Science Development in Tanzania and Eastern Africa: Proceedings of the 20th Anniversary Conference on Advances in Marine Science in Tanzania, 28 June–1 July 1999, Zanzibar, Tanzania.* Stone Town, Zanzibar: Institute of Marine Sciences, University of Dar es Salaam and Western Indian Ocean Marine Science Association, 2001.

Van Der Elst, Rudy, Bernadine Everett, Narriman Jiddawi, Gerald Mwatha, Paula Santana Afonso, and David Boulle. 'Fish, fishers and fisheries of the Western Indian Ocean: their diversity and status: a preliminary assessment.' *Philosophical Transactions of the Royal Society A* 363 (2005): pp. 263–284.

Working Document, 5059 TCMP. *Tanzania State of the Coast 2001: People and the Environment.* Dar es Salaam: Tanzania Coastal Management Partnership Science and Technical Working Group, 2001.

ACKNOWLEDGEMENTS

My most profound thanks to all the scientists who spent so much time explaining your research and reviewing several of the chapters for me. You are an incredibly patient and gracious lot. Some of you even allowed me into your homes and your personal thoughts. I am grateful. I want to make it clear, though, that I alone am responsible for any errors of fact or interpretation here.

In particular, I'd like to thank Nancy Knowlton. You were my starting place and everything and everyone I encountered after seemed to reach back to you. Dave Robins, you are an unparalleled host and guide and I thank you for all the doors you opened for me in England. Carol Turley, you literally changed my way of seeing over our dinner in Plymouth. I honour you as a remarkable human being. Thanks as well for the extraordinary kindness of Joanie Kleypas, Jim Hendee (and your coral-list), Chris Langdon, Mike Roman, Stu Ludsin, Katharina Fabricius, Michael Depledge, Heike Lotze, Boris Worm, Matt Huber, Narriman Jiddawi, Amy Wright, Shirley Pomponi, Phil and Daphne Hart and many others.

Arthur Hanson provided valuable insight and feedback on the China chapter. Trevor Platt was unfailingly generous on the tricky subjects of plankton and ocean metabolism. And Tim Flannery was a recurring source of support and advice. Thank you all.

In my personal life, I'd like to thank Sally Harding, my agent. You are this book's midwife. Thanks to Ross Mitchell for your insight on the dimension of time. Many thanks to the redoubtable Patterson clan for the endless challenge and support you provide. David and Anne have been unstintingly generous with ideas, particularly on systems theory, and other much-needed resources. John and Thea, you read very early versions of the first part of the book and offered valuable insight. And without the practical and intellectual gifts of my dear James, this book would never have come to be. Thank you.

Excerpts on pages 88–90 from *The Life of Vertebrates* by J.Z. Young are reproduced by permission of Oxford University Press; excerpts on p. 193 from *The Eternal Darkness* by Robert Ballard, copyright 2000, and on page 15 from *Air and Water* by Mark W. Denny, copyright 1993, are reproduced by permission of Princeton University Press.

INDEX